The Origin of Life

Selected Topics in Modern Biology

SERIES EDITOR

Professor Peter Gray
Andrey Avinoff Distinguished Professor of Biology
University of Pittsburgh

Series Editor's Statement

With this volume in SELECTED TOPICS IN MODERN BIOLOGY, Reinhold Publishing Corporation continues its expanding program in the biological sciences. The books in this series, unlike many other contemporary paperback textbooks, will provide beginning students with information on subjects that are frequently of necessity cursorily treated in other texts. The aim of SELECTED TOPICS IN MODERN BIOLOGY is the presentation of a full and unified coverage of the principles fundamental to the biological sciences by offering a treatment in depth of each separate topic included within the framework of the series.

John Keosian's "The Origin of Life" makes an important contribution to the fulfillment of this objective. The origin of life is one of the oldest problems of mankind, and there have been almost cyclic swings between materialist and other approaches. Professor Keosian is well qualified, as the reader will soon discover, to place all these divergent outlooks in their proper perspective. He has no ax to grind and no doctrine to preach. His only concern is to lay bare in clear and simple, but scholarly, language both his own ideas and those of others. No undergraduate—or for that matter no graduate —will have his opinions shaped for him by reading this book, but each reader will have an unusually good opportunity to form his own views on the basis of the knowledge and understanding gained therefrom.

PETER GRAY

The Origin of Life

JOHN KEOSIAN

Professor of Biology
Newark College of Arts and Sciences
Rutgers ● The State University
and Experimental Biologist
The Newark Beth Israel Hospital

New York
REINHOLD PUBLISHING CORPORATION
Chapman & Hall Ltd., London

Preface

Experimental evidence on the origin of life has accumulated rapidly over the last ten or eleven years. Contributions have come from laboratories all over the world, and much of the evidence supports the hypothesis on the origin of life proposed in 1936 by A. I. Oparin. However, developments in biochemistry since that time and some of the recent experimental evidence point to a broader interpretation of the origin of life. Many meetings and symposia at both local and international levels have been held on the subject, resulting in a lively and highly productive interchange of ideas. Since full justice could not be done to this voluminous material within the space of this book, sincere apologies are extended to the many authors whose valuable contributions could not be presented.

I am greatly indebted to various authors for generously permitting the use of illustrative materials from their original works, and am especially grateful to Dr. S. W. Fox for the use of some of his unpublished electron micrographs of proteinoid microspheres. I cannot begin to evaluate my indebtedness to my many students and to my colleagues at the Newark College of Arts and Sciences (Rutgers) and at the Marine Biological Laboratory (Woods Hole) with whom I have discussed the stimulating subject of the origin of life.

Special thanks are due to Paula Gottdenker, my research assistant, for contributing Chapter 2 and most of the section on extraterrestrial life, for the preparation of a number of the illustrations, and for typing the manuscript. I have also profited greatly from her criticisms of the first drafts from a reader's point of view.

Mr. John Hart and Mrs. Elisabeth Belfer of Reinhold have given unstintingly of their time and advice during the preparation of this book for publication. My sincere thanks go also to them.

JOHN KEOSIAN

Newark, N. J.
May, 1964

Contents

chapter one

Nature of the Problem

The origin of life, one of the oldest and most elusive problems of biology, has engaged the attention of some of the keenest minds in philosophy and science for more than 25 centuries. Within that time, several explanations have been attempted, each having staunch supporters at one time or another. However, during the last three centuries, these theories have come in for searching scrutiny and experimentation, and by now, most of them have been abandoned because they lack a scientific basis.

The thinking on the origin of life had incorporated several main approaches by the turn of this century. Among these approaches were vitalism, special creation, panspermia, mechanism, and materialism. Vitalism attributes the distinctive properties characteristic of living things to a supernatural "life force," and special creation is the literal interpretation of the biblical story in Genesis. Neither concept is susceptible to experimental proof. Panspermia avoids the question of the actual origin of life by assuming its eternal and universal existence. Although vitalism, special creation, and panspermia need no detailed consideration here, mechanism and materialism deserve more attention.

Mechanism

Mechanistic theories are based on the belief that the origin, activities, and properties of life derive from natural laws and that inorganic matter gave rise to a living thing in accordance with those laws. But these theories were confronted with a dilemma. How can a living thing be constructed in the first place from inorganic matter? For it was believed that the earth contained no organic compounds in prebiological times, since it was firmly held that only living things can synthesize organic compounds. But organic compounds are the very life of living things, and their origin, in the absence of such compounds, becomes a formidable problem, so much so, that many took a defeatist attitude toward the possibility of solving the problem.

The mechanistic hypothesis resolved this quandary by proposing that the first living thing was a macromolecule, a "living molecule," that was formed by the chance coming together of the elements that composed it in the proper proportions and arrangements. It was thought that this would most probably be a molecule of protein, the class of compound on which life was supposed to depend most intimately. In other words, the mechanistic hypothesis, which *clings* to the concept that only living things can make organic compounds, explains the origin of the first living thing in terms of the chance combination of the elements. This long chance, the view holds, could only come about because it had an enormously long span of time for trial and error.

Materialism

The materialistic hypothesis takes a different approach in applying natural laws to the explanation of the origin of life. This theory *rejects* the contention that only living things can make organic compounds. It proposes that organic compounds were formed abiogenically (that is, without the intervention of living things) before organisms came into being. Instead of a chance getting together of the elements to form a living thing all at once, materialism views the origin of life as the result of a series of probable steps of increasing complexity, inevitably leading up to the living state. One of the steps is the abiogenic synthesis of organic compounds. Each step comprises a higher level of organization of matter governed by laws that did not exist at the lower levels. Thus, with the formation of molecules, new physical and chemical properties came into existence which were not present in the world of uncombined elements. The laws applicable to inorganic chemistry do not completely and adequately describe the field of organic chemistry, nor do the laws applicable to small particles adequately describe all of the phenomena characteristic of macromolecules. With the advent of organisms, biological laws came into being which did not exist at a lower level of organization. From the materialist view, the origin of life was no remote accident; it was the result of matter evolving to higher and higher levels through the inexorable working out at each level of its inherent potentialities to arrive at the next level.

Development of the Materialist Viewpoint

At first this theory, too, did not lend itself to experimentation for want of sufficient advances in physics, chemistry, and allied fields. There were, though, a number of thinkers who started to speculate about the gradual evolution of life from nonliving matter. Among them, to name a few, were F. Engels, H. Spencer, T. H. Huxley, C. Mitchell, and E. A. Schäfer. Engels in his "Dialectics of Nature" was among the first to consider the spontaneous generation and the vitalistic theories from a materialist viewpoint and condemned them both. He maintained that life could have resulted only from a continuous evolution of matter, the origin of life being only a rung in the long ladder of development: In a similar vein, Schäfer (1912) stated: ". . . setting aside as devoid of scientific foundation the idea of immediate supernatural intervention in the first production of life, we are not only justified in believing, but compelled to believe, that living matter must have owed its origin to causes similar in character to those which have been instrumental in producing all other forms of matter in the universe, in other words, to a process of gradual evolution." These earlier arguments were logical, but unsupported by an explanation of the steps involved in this "gradual evolution," they did not succeed in dispelling the defeatist attitude toward the subject. This defeatism echoed Darwin's opinion which he so strongly expressed in a letter to J. D. Hooker: "It is mere rubbish to talk about the origin of life; one might as well talk about the origin of matter." Most of Darwin's contemporaries and many of his followers also dismissed the subject as not worthy of scientific consideration.

In 1922, the Russian biochemist A. I. Oparin delivered before the Botanical Society in Moscow a communication which dealt with his conclusions concerning the origin of life. He envisioned that organic compounds had already formed on the earth before life arose and that life evolved from these pre-existing compounds. Oparin's unique contribution is his revival of the materialistic approach to the question of how life originated, as well as his detailed development of this concept. He views the evolution of matter into inorganic compounds, organic compounds, primitive living things, and higher living forms, not as separate phenomena, but as steps in the unfolding of one and the same process. Life is but one of the many rising levels of matter evolving. Oparin's ideas were first published in 1924 in a booklet entitled "The Origin of Life."

The concept of the abiogenic formation of organic substances in the early, prebiotic history of the earth, was also expressed by J. B. S. Haldane in 1928,[1] who suggested that before the origin of life organic compounds "must have accumulated till the primitive oceans reached the consistency of hot dilute soup." He based this belief on the assumption that the primitive atmosphere contained carbon dioxide, ammonia, and water vapor, but no oxygen. Haldane claimed that such a mixture, exposed to ultraviolet light, would give rise to "a vast variety of organic substances."

The presence of organic compounds established a new order of reactivity not inherent in inorganic compounds. Oparin states: "From this point of view organic chemistry is not simply the chemistry of one of the elements from Mendeleev's periodic table. It exhibits special characteristic regularities which first manifest themselves on passing from the inorganic to the organic compounds of carbon." The transition from stage to stage—from one "form of the motion of matter" (Oparin) to another—is brought about by "natural selection" which applies in a way to nonliving as well as living systems.

Oparin did not merely state his theory of the origin of life— he developed his concept logically and step by step, supporting his contentions from the findings of all branches of science. He removed the main barriers which obstructed the path and led the way to a scientific attack on the problem. His second, more comprehensive book on "The Origin of Life on Earth," published in 1936 and ably translated into English by S. Morgulis in 1938, sparked a renewed interest in the subject. After the interruption of World War II, we witnessed an almost feverish activity among workers and thinkers in this field, and important findings continue to come forth. In spite of this large amount of work, or perhaps because of it, disagreements have arisen. There is general agreement on only one broad point, namely, that organic compounds, abiogenically synthesized, preceded the origin of life.

The Problem of Definition

A definition of "life" or of "living thing" has been purposely avoided up to this point. Many scientists have expressed the opinion that a precise definition—that is, one which will include all living things, past or present, and will exclude all nonliving things—is not possible. But this need not be a deterrent to the serious investigation of life and its origin. As Pauling put it: "In connection with the origin of life, I should like to say that it is sometimes easier to study a subject than to define it. For many years I have been studying the nature of the chemical bond. . . However, when I discussed this question (with others), we found that it is extremely difficult to define the chemical bond." Life and living thing mean different things to different people. When the comparison involves living things that are very much alive like a man or a tree and obviously nonliving things like a piece of glass or a chunk of metal, agreement is not difficult to obtain. But at the borderline where the simplest systems are being compared, agreement is generally not possible. Structurally, the simplest form of life to some can consist of a single macromolecule—a "living molecule." Horowitz arrives at such a definition in suggesting that the minimum properties of a living system are mutability, self-duplication, and heterocatalysis. He points out that these criteria are satisfied by the gene which consists of individual molecules of deoxyribonucleic acid. Since "no living thing can function in a vacuum," the definition of life in Horowitz's terms becomes "individual molecules in a polymolecular environment."

Some scientists maintain that metabolically the simplest form of life consists of a system in which exergonic and endergonic reactions are correlated. On the basis of this assumption, one can construct a definition of life, as did K. M. Madison,[2] that will include as an organism a system of two inorganic reactions. Madison proposes that "life is anything perceivable by an observer of a group of chemical systems in which free energy is released as a part of the reactions of one or more of the systems and in which some of this free energy is used in the reactions of one or more of the remaining systems." He recognizes the fact that "the definition does not require that the simplest organisms have any organic molecules" and that "things as simple as two inorganic reactions meet the definition."

On the other extreme, a definition of life would include the characteristics of all living things past and present. Thus a simple definition would not be sufficient. For example, a definition of life based on the assumed properties of only the first living things would "exclude from among its features, not merely consciousness, but also respiration, which obviously did not take place among the earliest organisms. On the other hand, if we define life on the basis of phenomena which are typical only of the more highly developed living things, we shall risk relegating the anaerobic bacteria, as well as many primitive organisms to the category of nonliving bodies belonging to inorganic nature."[3]

Perspective

This apparent confusion reflects the necessity of recognizing the gradual transition of matter into higher and higher levels of organization embodying newer and more complicated properties. One's definition of life may then lead one to accept a particular level of organization of matter as a "living" state but not any level below it, whereas another may accept one or more levels lower or consider one or more levels higher as "living." What is important is not an exact definition of life at the borderline on which we can all agree, but rather the recognition of the existence of increasing levels of organization of matter and the understanding of the mechanisms which operate to bring these about. In other words, it would appear more sensible to approach the problem of the origin of life not as an attempt to discover the precise point at which lifeless matter gave rise to the "first living thing," but rather as an examination of the mechanisms operating in the transition of

matter on this earth to higher and higher levels of organization. Then the first level of organization which can be considered "alive" will still be a matter of personal preference,
but at least we will all be talking about the same thing. Thus,
as others have pointed out, attempts at an exact definition of
life are not only fruitless, at least for the present, but meaningless.[4]

Oparin's hypothesis served as the point of departure in the
modern phase of the problem of the origin of life. After a brief
historical survey of past theories, his contribution will be presented. This will be followed by an analysis of his theory in
the light of the work and thinking of others. Practically every
aspect of the problem is open to speculation, a fact which has
tempted many authors. In the last part of this book, I will
present some speculations which have been made on the possibility of the existence of extraterrestrial life and some of my
own ideas on the possibility of the continued origin of primitive living things on the earth throughout time up to and including the present.

References

1. Haldane, J. B. S., "Rationalist Annual (1928), reprinted in
   "Science and Human Life," Harper Brothers, New York, 1933.
2. Madison, K. M., "The Organism and its Origin," *Evolution* **7,** 211
   (1953).
3. Oparin, A. I., "Life; Its Nature, Origin and Development,"
   Academic Press, New York, 1962.
4. Pirie, N. W., "The Meaninglessness of the Terms Life and
   Living," in Needham, J., and Green, D., eds., "Perspectives in
   Biochemistry," The University Press, Cambridge, England, 1937.

chapter two

Historical Background

Life in all its aspects probably occupied much of the thinking of men long before they were ready to record their history. As they looked about them at their every-day environment, they observed that straw, soil, mud, dirt, indeed any sort of refuse, was teeming with a festering, wriggling, darting multitude of organisms. Obviously, they thought, the living things had arisen from those sources which appeared to be veritable hot beds of spontaneous generation.

Taking their observations uncritically, the early Greek philosophers built various attractive theories on what they had seen with their own eyes. What they discovered only gave additional proof to their belief in the eternal universality of life which, according to Anaxagoras (510–428 B.C.) came down in tiny seeds (spermata) with the rain water to fructify the earth. This idea curiously antedates the much more recent theories involving panspermia.

To Aristotle (384–322 B.C.) spontaneous generation was equally certain, and he maintained that not only worms and insects, but also fish, frogs, and mice could spring from suitable breeding materials like filth and moist soil. Even man might have a similar origin, developing from a wormlike beginning. Aristotle's contribution to the thinking and experimentation on the origin of life was the most far-reaching and long-lasting of all.

The scholars of the Middle Ages, steeped in superstitions and with only the badly translated and half-understood writings of Aristotle to guide them, added some fantastic embell-ishments to the "established fact" of spontaneous generation. Sometimes, as in the case of the goosetree (Fig. 2-1), convenience was served better than science, for if geese grew on trees they were proper food for meatless fast days. Travelers returned from the Orient with tales about a vegetable lamb found in gourdlike fruit (Fig. 2-2).

Alchemists, though failing to turn base metals into precious ones, were convinced that even a homunculus, a miniature manikin, could be produced in a flask. The famous Paracelsus, as late as the 16th century, gave a detailed prescription for this astonishing feat, and also reported on his observations of various instances where mice, frogs, eels, etc., were generated spontaneously from water, air, and decaying wood. Is it any wonder then that Shakespeare, who wrote about timeless truths, also repeated the old wive's tales and views of his time by letting his characters in Anthony and Cleopatra, Julius Caesar, and Hamlet tell about the generation of animals from moist mud, decaying hides and hair, rotting meat, etc., activated by the heat of the sun?

Fig. 2-1. Goose Tree.

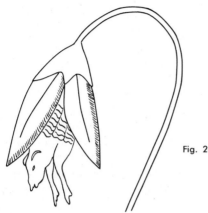

Fig. 2-2. Vegetable Lamb.

The physician Francesco Redi (1626–1698), using truly scientific methods, was the first to shake the firm belief in spontaneous generation. By securely covering with gauze a vessel into which he had placed pieces of meat and eel, he proved that the little white maggots came out of the eggs deposited by flies on the cover and not directly from the rotting meat. He accepted, however, other claims of the spontaneous generation of intestinal worms from decaying matter and gall-flies from plant juice. And, even though the experimental proofs against the old belief mounted up, it continued well into the 19th century. Improved methods of investigation and increasing awareness of the complexity of the structure making up living organisms finally did away with the cruder concepts of spontaneous generation of higher plants and animals; the emphasis was shifted to microorganisms.

Leeuwenhoek's (1632–1723) invention of the microscope gave fuel to this by affording visual proof to the proponents of the spontaneous generation theory that "tiny live animals" were found wherever decay or fermentation of lifeless substances occurred. (Another example of wrong interpretation of correct observations). This view was not shared by Leeuwenhoek himself, and some years later Joblot, who also disbelieved spontaneous generation, successfully tested his conviction that the infesting microorganisms had been airborne. He divided a boiled infusion of hay into two containers, closing one vessel immediately with parchment and leaving the other exposed to the air. The microorganisms which grew profusely in the open vessel appeared in the first container only after he removed the parchment cover. Joblot's findings, however, were not accepted by his contemporaries.

Buffon (1707–1799) viewed living things as a mosaic of organic molecules which, after each individual being came to an end, were available for reshuffling into many other combinations, thus forming new living things. Needham (1713–1781) supported this thought that microorganisms arose from organic particles; moreover, he believed that such organic particles had to be vitalized by the agency of a life force. Needham undertook to test his belief by putting boiling-hot mutton gravy (or infusions) and other organic materials into tightly stoppered vials. That all his vials showed a lively growth of microorganisms underlined his conviction that spontaneous generation from organic matter not only could but *had to* occur.

Spallanzani (1729–1799) came to the opposite conclusion, namely, that no growth could occur if the tests were carried out with the proper precautions. These measures consisted in prolonged boiling of the organic broths and infusions and in immediate sealing-off of the vessels containing them. He failed, too, to convince his fellow scientists. Much was made of the fact that oxygen was removed from the vessels treated in this manner, and many sterilization experiments were carried out to test if it really was the lack of oxygen which prevented bacterial growth. Most of the experimentation seemed to uphold the impossibility of spontaneous generation;

nevertheless, the occasional failures made the results inconclusive.

The controversy reached a peak in 1859 when Pouchet published his voluminous record of experiments, which in essence repeated the earlier findings of Buffon and Needham. Like his predecessors he believed that organic particles stemming from disintegrated organisms can be reorganized into new living things, but only in the presence of a vital force. All his innumerable tests seemed to bear out his contention.

The French Academy of Sciences thereupon offered a prize to the researcher who would settle the argument once and for all. Pasteur (1822–1895) accepted the challenge and earned not only the prize (1864) but also succeeded in dispelling the previously firmly held belief in spontaneous generation. A description of his experiments and an evaluation of the validity of the conclusions drawn from them will be given in Chapter 9.

The problem was not solved, however, by summarily dismissing the possibility of spontaneous generation and by accepting the hard fact that life must only come from life; the question still remained of how life started originally, that is, before there was any living progenitor on earth.

One of the answers was to assume that life did not need to originate as it was co-existent with the eternal universe. Another suggestion was that it was imported from outer space. Preyer (1880) explains his idea of the eternity of life on the basis of the observation that life only comes from life, never from lifeless matter. Therefore, life must have existed even at the time when the earth was a mass of molten liquid. In fact, this ball of fiery liquid was a single living organism as proved by its inherent motion. Thus, this swirling motion was the beginning of life, which on cooling (dying in part) precipitated inorganic substances on the surface and continued as protoplasmic residue.

Richter (1865) advanced another theory of how life came to be on earth, since the planet was much too hot after separating from the sun to support living organisms. Through the fast movement of celestial bodies, small particles could have become dislodged and propelled out into space. Viable germs in a dormant state may have been carried along on these particles. Upon reaching, quite by accident, another planet with conditions favorable for life, the spores then could develop and initiate a panoply of living organisms.

Helmholtz (1864) also thought along these lines. He postulated that live germs came to earth by the agency of meteorites, an idea that in recent years caused the repeated, painstaking examination of the Orgueil specimen (Chapter 4).

Arrhenius (1908), in reviving the theory of cosmozoa, based his concept of panspermia on very ingenious calculations showing that transfer of particles between celestial bodies was indeed possible. Once carried upward from a planet by powerful air currents and shot out into space by electric discharges, the tiny spores of microorganisms are pushed farther away by the pressure of light rays to travel towards other planetary systems. While this theory found many staunch adherents, the probability of interplanetary exchange of viable spores becomes increasingly remote in the light of more recent findings. The sources that made the origin of life possible on the earth must be looked for right here on earth.

/ *chapter three*

*Oparin Hypothesis**

This chapter is a summary of the first comprehensive statement of the theory of the origin of life on the earth by Oparin,
published first in Russian in 1936 and translated into English
in 1938 by Serguis Morgulis.*

In his approach to the problem of the origin of organic compounds on the earth, Oparin based his contentions on the then
prevalent theory of the fiery origin of the planets. According
to this theory, proposed by Sir James Jeans, a mass of the
sun's atmosphere was torn away by another star which
hurtled toward the sun in a near-collision and then sped on its
course. The mutual gravitational force of such an approach
caused a tidal bulge on the surface of both stars. A portion
of the bulge on our sun was pulled away in the form of a
spindle—a thin leading stream widening into a larger,
more massive central portion, which trailed off again into
a thin rear streamer. The elongated mass of incandescent
gas was propelled into orbit around the sun and soon fragmented into separate masses which condensed into the respective planets. The thin stream farthest from the sun
gave rise to the remotest small planets, while the largest
planets were formed from the central portion and the thin
streamer nearest the sun gave rise to the small planets Earth,
Mercury, and Venus. This mode of formation of the planets

*All of the quotations and source material in this chapter are taken from
Oparin, A. I., "The Origin of Life," Dover Publications, Inc., New York,
1953 ($1.75). Other publications of Oparin on the origin of life are listed
under Selected Readings, p. 113.

also explains the observed similarity in the types and abundances of various elements of the planets and of the sun's atmosphere (Table 3-1). Although this theory is no longer considered to be valid, it served as a basis for Oparin's development of his theory of the primary origin of organic compounds on the earth.

Chemical Reactions on the Primitive Earth

In the fiery origin theory, one has to consider the state of matter at the postulated temperatures as well as the subse-

TABLE 3-1. Comparative Analysis of Composition of the Sun (Log Q)

Serial No.	Element	Sun's Atmosphere	Earth's Crust	Stone Meteorites
11	sodium	8.6	8.7	7.8
12	magnesium	9.2	8.6	9.1
13	aluminum	7.8	9.2	8.2
14	silicon	8.8	9.7	9.3
19	potassium	8.4	8.7	7.2
20	calcium	8.3	8.8	8.1
21	scandium	5.3	3.0	
22	titanium	6.9	8.1	7.0
23	vanadium	6.7	6.9	
24	chromium	7.4	7.1	7.5
25	manganese	7.6	7.3	7.3
26	iron	9.0	9.0	9.4
27	cobalt	7.4	5.8	7.1
28	nickel	7.8	6.8	8.2
29	copper	6.8	6.3	6.2
30	zinc	6.7	5.9	
		Metalloids		
1	hydrogen	11.5	8.3	6.9
6	carbon	8.5	7.4	7.2
7	nitrogen	8.7	6.8	
8	oxygen	10.2	9.7	9.6
9	fluorine		6.8	
15	phosphorus		7.4	7.0
16	sulfur	7.2	7.3	8.3
17	chlorine		7.7	6.9

Oparin, A. I., "The Origin of Life," Dover Publications, Inc., New York, 1953

quent transformations in matter that occurred while the mass of incandescent gas cooled and condensed. The original temperature of the protoplanet was high, about 5000–6000°C, according to this theory. Portions of the atmosphere of stars within that temperature range have been spectroscopically examined for their carbon compounds. The spectral bands indicate that in the range between 4000 and 8000°C, carbon exists in three major forms, dicarbon (C_2), cyanogen (CN), and methene (CH). Compounds of carbon and oxygen are not detected at these temperatures although oxides of other elements, that is, aluminum, boron, hydrogen (OH radical), titanium, and zirconium, are found. Carbon and many of the metals have a high vaporization point and were among the first to condense as the gas cooled and "dropped" to the center of the mass, ultimately forming its core. At a temperature of 3000–4000°C, molten carbon became mixed with the metallic core to form metal carbides, which are stable compounds at these temperatures. Carbon dioxide and carbon monoxide dissociate at 2800–3000°C and thus could not exist at the higher temperatures at which the stabler metal carbides were formed.

Origin of the Primitive Atmosphere

The atmosphere of gases around the molten core was stratified according to the density of its components. From the upper atmosphere the lighter gases continually escaped into space: hydrogen, helium, nitrogen, oxygen, argon, and others. The gravitational field of the yet incompletely condensed planet was not sufficient to counter the escaping tendency of these lighter atoms, especially in view of their high kinetic energy at the elevated temperatures. These atoms, providing they formed compounds, such as H_2O, NH_3, SiO_2, and MgN, were retained thereby. In the molten core, substances also became stratified according to their relative densities. The crust

that formed when the earth cooled sufficiently roughly reflects this separation, with the heavier periodite comprising
the deepest portion and with basalt and granite above it.

Oxygen as a gas was absent from the atmosphere of the
primordial earth not only due to its escape but also because
the great avidity for oxygen of many substances in the reduced
state converted them readily into the corresponding oxides.
It is estimated that even today, should oxygen cease to be
generated by plants, all the available free oxygen will be taken
up in less than 1000 years by igneous rocks and other incompletely oxidized substances. Oparin considered the nitrogen
of the present atmosphere as also having a secondary, probably biogenic origin. As carbon formed carbides with certain
metals, nitrogen also went into combination with metals to
form nitrides.

Ammonia was formed when hot metal nitrides, which extruded to the surface of the crust, reacted with the superheated steam:

$$MeN + 3H_2O \rightarrow Me(OH)_3 + NH_3 \qquad (Me = metal)$$

Ammonium salts also yielded ammonia under these conditions. Ammonia could have formed also in the hot primitive
atmosphere by the direct reaction between hydrogen and
nitrogen:

$$3H_2 + N_2 \rightarrow 2NH_3$$

A further source for ammonia is the reaction between cyanam-
ides and water vapor:

$$CaCN_2 + 3H_2O \rightarrow CaCO_3 + 2NH_3$$

Calcium cyanamide comes from the reaction between calcium
carbide and nitrogen:

$$CaC_2 + N_2 \rightarrow CaCN_2 + C$$

Origin of Organic Compounds

Oparin's theory of the origin of organic compounds is significant for his assumption that the first carbon compounds were hydrocarbons and not carbon dioxide, that is, he assumed that carbon appeared first in the reduced and not in the oxidized state and that the primordial atmosphere contained no oxygen. This premise is fundamental to Oparin's thinking and had to be brought into keeping with the details of the formation of the planets, particularly of the earth.

As the atmosphere cooled to 1000°C and lower, the highly reactive free radicals CH and CH_2 could combine to form a variety of simple hydrocarbons both unsaturated and saturated:

$$CH + CH \rightarrow HC\equiv CH$$
Acetylene

$$CH_2 + CH_2 \rightarrow H_2C\equiv CH_2$$
Ethylene

$$CH_2 + CH_2 \rightarrow CH_4 + C$$
Methane

$$2CH_4 \rightarrow HC\equiv CH + 3H_2$$

Metal carbides are also a source for hydrocarbons of varying chain lengths and degree of saturation:

$$CaC_2 + H_2O \rightarrow HC\equiv CH + CaO$$
Acetylene

or
$$3Fe_4C_5 + 16H_2O \rightarrow 4Fe_3O_4 + C_{15}H_{32}$$

In this way, as the crust had begun to form but was still too hot to permit condensation of steam to water, the atmosphere above the crust contained both carbon and nitrogen in the reduced state, that is, hydrocarbons and ammonia, respectively. This is the reducing atmosphere that forms the basis of Oparin's further development of his theory of the origin of life.

In reaction with the superheated steam the unsaturated hydrocarbons readily formed oxy and hydroxy derivatives, for example, acetaldehyde from acetylene:

$$HC\equiv CH + H_2O \rightarrow CH_3CHO$$

The saturated hydrocarbons may also undergo similar reactions. As a result, the atmosphere soon contained in addition to an assortment of hydrocarbons, an abundance of aldehydes, alcohols, and acids. These hydrocarbon derivatives combine readily with ammonia to form ammonium salts, amides, amines, etc.

As the earth cooled sufficiently, torrential and prolonged rains were accompanied by frequent violent bursts of lightning. The rains began to accumulate as hot bodies of water, containing abundant and varied organic compounds washed down from the atmosphere. The waters of this stage of the earth's development have been referred to by Haldane as a "hot dilute soup," a view to which Oparin subscribes.

The variety of organic compounds implied by this term arose not only through reactions (described above) in the atmosphere but also through the continued interaction among these compounds in the warm waters. The reaction types are condensation, polymerization, oxidation, and their reverse processes, that is, chain splitting, hydrolysis, and reduction. These possibilities can be summarized by some examples.

$$\underset{\text{Acetaldehyde}}{CH_3CHO} + CH_3CHO \xrightarrow{\text{condensation}} \underset{\text{Aldol}}{CH_3CHOHCH_2CHO}$$

In this type of reaction carbon-carbon bonds are formed, resulting in the formation of compounds of increasingly larger chains. The reverse, the rupture of a molecule between carbon atoms, also takes place as in the decarboxylation of pyruvic acid:

$$\underset{\text{Pyruvic acid}}{CH_3COCOOH} + H_2O \rightarrow \underset{\text{Acetaldehyde}}{CH_3CHO} + \underset{\text{Carbonic acid}}{CO(OH)_2}$$

Both the lengthening of carbon chains and the formation of ring compounds can result through condensation reactions. Biochemically significant compounds, such as fatty acids, sugars, and tannins, can form in this way.

In polymerization reactions, the length of molecules is increased also by addition, but the linkage is between carbon and some other atom, usually oxygen or nitrogen:

$$CH_3COOH + CH_3CH_2OH \xrightarrow{\text{polymerization}}$$

Acetic acid   Ethyl alcohol

$$CH_3COOCH_2CH_3 + H_2O$$

Ethyl acetate

Other combinations may occur in this way, for example, between two alcohol molecules or between two amino acid molecules:

$$2H_2NCH_2COOH \xrightarrow{\text{polymerization}} H_2NCH_2CONHCH_2COOH$$

Glycine   Glycylglycine

This type of reaction is the basis of the formation of proteins.

In the third type of reaction, oxidation always takes place simultaneously with reduction as, for example, in the reaction:

$$2CH_3CHO \xrightarrow[\text{oxidation-reduction}]{\text{HOH}} CH_3COOH + CH_3CH_2OH$$

Acetaldehyde   Acetic acid   Ethyl alcohol

The acid is the result of the oxidation of one molecule of acetaldehyde, and the alcohol is the result of the reduction of the other molecule.

The synthesis of amino acids is not at all unusual. The synthesis of glycine, for instance, can follow the simple sequence:

$$2H_2CO \xrightarrow{\text{polymerization}} CH_2OHCHO$$

Formaldehyde   Glycol aldehyde

$$2CH_2OHCHO + H_2O \xrightarrow{\text{oxidation-reduction}}$$

$$CH_2OHCH_2OH + CH_2OHCOOH$$

Glycol   Glycolic acid

$$CH_2OHCOOH + NH_3 \longrightarrow CH_2NH_2COOH + H_2O$$

Glycine

The Hot Dilute Soup

This survey indicates the great diversity of organic compounds that may form with continued, unceasing interaction among the numerous compounds. The new types of compounds that result also enter the pool of reactivity, further increasing the quantity and diversity of organic compounds. Some of the reactions, particularly condensations and polymerizations, lead to larger and larger molecules. There is every reason to assume, if the foregoing can be accepted as probable, that not only the kinds of organic compounds but also many of the chemical pathways characteristic of the first living things were brought about abiogenically. Thus, for the first billion or more years of earth's history, an atmosphere of simple hydrocarbons, nitrogen, hydrogen, and ammonia was continuously maintained, while the interaction among these products continuously formed the whole gamut of organic compounds.

Of all the transformations of matter on the earth, the most difficult to picture is that from inanimate substances, no matter how complex and reactive, to the first living things. The problem is further complicated by our lack of knowledge of the nature of the first living things. Nothing remotely comparable is known today. Oparin sought the answer in reacting systems capable of gradual increase in complexity of composition and in interaction with the environment. His starting material at this phase is the "hot dilute soup."

Colloidal State

This ocean of "soup" is not a chemically static thing. The simplest substances—hydrogen, steam, methane, ammonia, hydrogen sulfide, and nitrogen—continuously give rise to the simple hydrocarbons and their derivatives, the alcohols, aldehydes, ketones, sugars, and acids. Among the derivatives are the amino acids. The polymerization of amino acids would result in the formation of protein. What is remarkable about proteins is not the manner of their formation but the fundamental and exclusive role proteins have played in the "further evolution of organic compounds and in the origin of living organisms" (Oparin). A clue to the fundamental role of proteins may be found in the presence of both basic amino groups and acidic carboxyl groups in proteins. This endows the proteins with the properties of amphoteric substances, with positively and negatively charged sites on the molecule. The ability of molecules of protein to come together and form large complexes by virtue of their residual valences is also important. In this way colloidal hydrophilic complexes can form with a diffuse aura of water molecules around them. Such complexes may figure in the transition of inanimate systems into living things.

The colloidal state is a new, distinctive feature based primarily on particle size. At a critical range of particle size the behavior of the particles regarding light, diffusion, and environmental conditions shows a marked departure from the behavior of smaller particles. Thus, light is in part absorbed and in part reflected and scattered by colloidal particles. Moreover, the large size of the particle proportionately reduces the mobility of the particle in suspension. In addition, colloidal particles may frequently carry more than one charge, negative or positive, and this phenomenon is strongly influenced by the nature of the environment. Colloids generally have specific adsorptive properties. Particles of a colloid may remain discrete or may coalesce to form a coagulum that separates from the dispersion medium.

Formation of Coacervates

Coalescence may take another form. Colloidal particles may have an affinity for molecules of the dispersion medium. When this is water, the colloid is said to be hydrophilic. Particles of a hydrophilic colloid can be visualized as having a shell of water molecules surrounding them. The density of the shell diminishes with the distance from the particle, setting up a density gradient of water molecules in the vicinity of each particle. A hydrophilic colloid may separate out from the main body when the concentration of the colloid becomes great enough and ionic conditions are right. When individual particles are brought in close proximity, then within the outermost layer or two of hydrated water molecules a form of coalescence takes place. The particles with the hydrated layers around them form a liquid continuum that separates from the dispersion medium, forming two liquid phases with a sharp boundary between them. Such a separation of colloid from the medium is called coacervation; the separated colloid phase is the coacervate and the remaining liquid phase is the equilibrium liquid. The equilibrium liquid is impoverished in, but not completely deprived of colloid, while the coacervate is abundantly rich in colloid but still includes a small amount of the equilibrium liquid with its associated substances. The coacervate may undergo an exchange of substances with its environment. It will selectively concentrate some substances from the environment, depriving the environment and enriching itself in that substance.

From the standpoint of the origin of life, an important type of coacervation takes place when the colloid separates out in the form of microscopic droplets (Fig. 3-1) rather than as a layer. Each droplet has the general composition of a coalesced pool and is as unstable. The stability is affected by changes in temperature, hydrogen ion concentration, electrolytes, and neutral salts, as well as by changes in physical stress such as pressure and electric field. Certainly, with coacervation a new level of structure and activity is established —a step nearer to the explanation of the origin of life. A step still closer may be taken by considering complex coacervates.

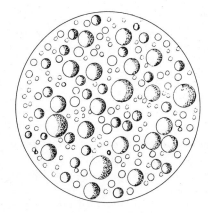

Fig. 3-1. Coacervate Droplets.

Complex coacervates are mixed coacervates in which more than one species of colloid participate. The most versatile of the complex coacervates have different proteins of opposite charges as the colloidal material. The stability of such coacervate droplets depends in part on a balance between opposing forces. The layer of hydrated water keeps the oppositely charged molecules apart, while the opposite charges on the different molecules draw them together. The stability of the colloid depends in part on the thickness of the layer of hydrated water in relation to the magnitude of the electrostatic forces between the protein molecules. Both of these factors can be affected by changes in the environment.

From Coacervates to Living Things

In complex coacervates with more than one type of protein, the charged colloidal molecules may be grouped in a definite organization instead of being randomly scattered. A type of internal grouping may take place, giving the interior of the coacervate a definite structure. The outer delimiting membrane consists of surface-active substances and not just the shell of hydrated water molecules. A selective permeability is thus possible between the equilibrium liquid and complex coacervates of this type. The colloid composition of a coacervate depends on the chemical composition of the medium from which it arises. This composition may vary from place to place at any time, and from time to time in any one place, in keeping with the changing character of the original "soup." For this reason a great variety of coacervates may form, differing in composition and stability from one another.

There is now the possibility of divergence in "chemical evolution" which could not take place previously. In the outside medium the products of chemical reactions can diffuse everywhere to become randomly distributed and to react with any possible substrate. Within the coacervate droplet, however, chemical reactions can take a more selective course, being limited to those substances which are within or which can gain entrance into the droplet. Those end products which cannot leave the droplet will become more and more concentrated inside. Thus, the solubility product of a substance may be exceeded within the droplet and a precipitate will form, but this may never occur in the enormous amount of solvent in the equilibrium liquid. For the same reason, reactions which do not take place between potential reactants because of their extreme dilution in the medium, may readily occur in the coacervate if the precursor reactions which synthesize them take place in the confined space of the droplets. Here the reactants can readily accumulate to their reaction levels. These are but two examples of the many ways in which the chemistry within the confined space of a droplet possessing semipermeability may differ from that taking place in the equilibrium liquid.

Catalysis is another way in which the droplets may show an individuality. Droplets may differ from each other in the complement of contained catalysts. This difference can obviously lead to further divergence among droplets in their chemical activity. Adsorption of catalysts on the colloids, especially the proteins, will lead to the formation of metallo-organic catalysts, and, eventually, enzymes. Two very important characteristics are bestowed upon such combinations. One is the greatly increased efficiency of catalysis, and the other is specificity. By greatly accelerating a reaction, such a metallo-organic catalyst can render practically inoperative other routes otherwise open to any of the reactants of a given reaction. The most powerful and most specific of such catalysts are the enzymes, and with the greatly increased concentration of protein in coacervate droplets over that in the equilibrium liquid, the eventual formation of enzymes was inevitable.

But increased rate and selectivity of chemical reactions in a droplet does not necessarily spell increased balance in the dynamic steady state. Indeed, the majority of coacervate droplets will be rendered more unstable through this random development of primordial enzymes. But that matters little as long as even a very few are rendered more stable through increased coordination of interdependent reactions by the development of the "proper" enzymes. Such droplets will persist longer and will have a longer chemical history within which further changes will be wrought. This is the beginning of a form of "natural selection" by which droplets in which the "proper" enzymes develop will last longer, and with them the enzymes themselves. Continuation of this process in the more "successful" droplets will increase the number of reactions brought into harmony with each other and thus increase the probability of longer "survival" of the droplet. Again, this alone is not enough from the point of view of the origin of life. The harmony established among reactions must be such that the total effect is the increase in amount of the critical components of the droplet. In this way a coordinated growth will take place. But beyond simple growth there must be replication.

The increase in size of a droplet will make it more susceptible to physical fragmentation by external mechanical disturbances. These fragments, having the same composition as the original droplet, will have the properties of the original coacervate. Thus, each will grow and fragment again, increasing the amount of organized material at the expense of the organic compounds randomly distributed in the equilibrium liquid. A competition in efficiency of growth will set in among the droplets, the more efficient droplets increasing more rapidly. The development of synthetic pathways in a droplet, making it independent of one or more components of the medium, would be of survival value to any droplet in this "competition." A form of natural selection would operate in favor of those droplets which become independent of diminishing organic components in the outside liquid, and the less "adapted" droplets would disintegrate. In some such manner, the most primitive living things eventually came about.

In Chapters 4–6, Oparin's theory will be evaluated in terms of experimental evidence that has since accumulated.

chapter four

Distribution of Simple Organic Compounds

An explanation of the origin of life on the earth rests primarily on an explanation of the origin of organic compounds on this planet before life appeared. The era in which this must have occurred extended from the origin of the earth some 4.5 billion years ago until life appeared about 2.5 billion years ago. Geological records cannot tell us about the atmosphere at that remote period; some deductions must be made from the astronomical findings. In the later part of the nineteenth and the beginning of the twentieth century it was still generally believed that organic compounds could not occur in nature unless living things intervened in their formation. It is now recognized, however, that the simplest organic compounds are probably widely distributed throughout the universe, and natural conditions do exist under which these simpler compounds could conceivably be synthesized into a whole array of biochemically significant substances.

Methods of Gathering Data

Our knowledge of the universe outside of our planet has been gained primarily by observing objects and phenomena in the sky. The information reaches us in the form of electromagnetic waves from matter in the vast expanses surrounding the earth. Electromagnetic waves vary in wavelength from billionths of a millimeter as in gamma rays (γ-rays) to many kilometers as in long-wave radio. Of this whole spectrum, only two restricted portions reach the surface of the earth; the rest are reflected or absorbed by the ionosphere or atmosphere. One portion is represented by the short-wave radio rays with a wavelength between 0.1 cm and 100 meters. Most of the studies to date through this "window" have been made, however, at wavelengths between 0.1 and 32.8 meters. The other is the range between 5×10^{-7} and 1×10^{-6} cm which covers the near infrared, the whole visible range, and the near ultraviolet. This is summarized in Fig. 4-1.

All of the early observations were made through the narrow window represented by the visible portion of the spectrum. Development of better and better optical telescopes of various types and power assisted the eye in reaching farther and farther into the universe. Accessories to the telescope record phenomena not discernible by eye or register quantitatively the uncertain approximations of distance, luminosity, etc., detected by eye. The spectroscope is one of the most useful of these accessories. Attached to the telescope, it breaks the incoming light into a visible spectrum. When the spectrum from a region or an object in the universe is analyzed, the presence of specific substances can be inferred.

The use of a camera on a spectroscope (the combination is a spectrograph) makes it possible to record such observations permanently. Also, the use of film, sensitive to ultraviolet or to infrared rays, enables us to detect substances which do not appear on the visible spectrum. Further, the intensity of the respective bands is a measure of the approximate abundances of the substances thus detected.

Radio telescopes have also assisted in unique discoveries. With these instruments, we can look through the second "window" depicted in Fig. 4-1 and detect wavelengths in the range of microwaves and short-wave radio. Thus, we are able to "see" the stars that lie beyond interstellar gas and clouds which obstruct light but permit the passage of short-wave

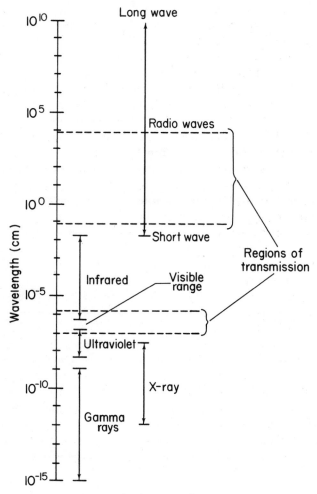

Fig. 4-1. The Electromagnetic Spectrum.

radio waves. Several thousand objects that emit no light but do emit a high intensity of radiowaves have been discovered in this way. Before the advent of radio telescopes these "radio stars" went undetected.

The use of balloons, rockets, and satellites is beginning to overcome further limitations on our ability to observe the universe. These limitations are the optically distorting and turbulent character of the atmosphere and the absorption by it of much of the electromagnetic spectrum. Balloons, rockets, and satellites can carry instruments and accessories to the calmer upper reaches of the atmosphere or completely beyond it. Appropriate rocket-borne devices can intercept rays before they are absorbed by our atmosphere. By this method, X-rays emanating apparently from the direction of the Crab Nebula and of the constellation Scorpio were reported in October of 1962 and confirmed by a more recent rocket shot in June 1963. Great as their contributions have been, the devices that lift instruments into space are still limited in their capacity to carry all the necessary accessories available on land. Eventually, orbiting observatories may eliminate some of these limitations.

The study and analysis of meteorites furnish yet another clue to the nature of the immediate space around us. Meteorites represent fragments of matter scattered in the orbit of the earth. Modern theory favors the view that the earth originated from the condensation of a disc of gas and dust orbiting around the sun, which had formed previously from a much larger amount of the same substances. A portion of this orbiting disc has formed the earth, which continues to sweep through the fragments in its orbit.

Universal Distribution of Hydrocarbons

We have gained much useful information by the above mentioned means concerning the chemical composition of the stars, galaxies, gas and dust clouds, and interstellar space. There is good reason to believe that, in addition to a variety of inorganic matter, the free radicals :CH and :CH$_2$; dicarbon (C$_2$); and the lower hydrocarbons methane (CH$_4$), ethane (H$_3$C—CH$_3$), acetylene (HC≡CH), and ethylene (H$_2$C= CH$_2$), as well as others are present in stars or in clouds of gas and dust; there is also some evidence of higher hydrocarbons. Compounds of carbon and nitrogen, for example, cyanogen (CN), are also detected.

Hydrocarbons have been found to exist also on planets of our solar system. Methane is detected on Jupiter, Uranus, Neptune, and on Saturn and its satellite Titan. Although most of the carbon in the atmosphere of Venus, Earth, and Mars is in the form of carbon dioxide, methane has been detected on Venus and Mars. Ethylene and acetylene have been found to exist on Jupiter. Urey considers it probable that the floating red spot on Jupiter represents in part cuprene, a polymer of acetylene. Ethylene and acetylene have also been detected in the atmosphere of Venus and Mars. Hydrocarbons still form abiogenically on the earth by the action of hot water on metal carbides or of cold water on hot carbides extruded by volcanic action.

Meteorites furnish the only direct evidence of the chemical composition of extraterrestrial bodies.[1,2,3] The presence of complex hydrocarbons in certain meteorites has unequivocally been established. As long ago as 1834 Berzelius found carbonaceous material in the Alais meteorite. Recent analyses of a sample of the Orgueil meteorite which fell at Orgueil, France, in 1864, show it to contain 6 per cent organic material in addition to a number of inorganic compounds (Table 4-1). Saturated hydrocarbons containing 15 to 25 or more carbon atoms were found in the organic fraction by these analyses, as well as mono-, di-, and tetracycloalkanes. There is sharp controversy as to the biogenic or nonbiogenic nature of some

TABLE 4-1. Composition of the Orgueil Meteorite

| | Per Cent Composition | |
Component	Not Dried	Dried at 110°C Temperature
SiO_2	24.475	26.0310
Fe_2O_3	13.324	14.2360
FeO	17.924	19.0630
MgO	8.163	8.6711
S	4.369	4.6466
SO_4	2.195	2.3345
NiO	2.450	2.6057
CaO	2.183	2.3220
Al_2O_3	1.175	1.2498
Na_2O	1.244	1.3230
K_2O	0.307	0.3265
MnO	1.815	1.9302
Cr_2O_3	0.225	0.2392
CoO	0.085	0.0904
Cl	0.073	0.0776
P	Trace	Trace
NH_3	0.098	0.1042
H_2O^-	5.975	—
H_2O^+*	7.345	7.8120
Organic	6.027	6.4100
Total	96.442	99.4728

*H_2O^+ designates water obtained above 110°C. temperature.

(From Nagy, B., Meinschein, W. G., and Hennessy, D. J., *Ann. N. Y. Acad. Sci.* **93,** 1961).

or all of these hydrocarbons. Included in the analyses was also a comparison of the meteorite hydrocarbons with hydrocarbons of biological origin, and it was believed that the similarities found "provide evidence for biogenic activity." In a later analysis of meteorites, Claus and others[4,5] report organized organic material that they interpret as fossil microorganisms. This interpretation has been accepted by some, but strongly contested by others. Although this controversy has yet to be resolved, all agree that the complex organic compounds found in fair abundance in the Orgueil meteorite and others do not represent contamination but are in fact of extraterrestrial origin.

Organic compounds seem indeed to be universally distributed. They are detected not only in stellar material but also in interstellar space, and mainly under conditions that preclude the possibility of their origin from living things. It remained to elucidate the origin of organic compounds on the earth. Whatever the explanation, it must of course conform with the events in the origination of the earth itself. It is interesting to note that a logical argument can be made for the appearance of organic compounds first as hydrocarbons and only later in more oxidized state, whether it is assumed that the earth had a fiery beginning or that it condensed from cold gases and dust, as it is now believed.

References

1. Mason, B., "Organic Matter from Space," *Sci. Am.* (March 1963).
2. Nagy, B., and Bitz, Sister M. C., "Long Chain Fatty Acids from the Orgueil Meteorite," *Arch. Biochem. Biophys.* **101,** (1963).
3. Nagy, G., Meinschein, W. G., and Hennessy, D. J., "Aqueous Low Temperature Environment of the Orgueil Meteorite Parent Body," *Ann. N. Y. Acad. Sci.* **108,** Art. 2, 534 (1963).
4. Claus, G., and Nagy, B., "A Microbiological Examination of some Carbonaceous Chondrites," *Nature* **192,** 594 (1961).
5. Claus, G., Nagy, B., and Europa, D. L., "Further Observations on the Properties of the 'Organized Elements' in Carbonaceous Chondrites," *Ann. N. Y. Acad. Sci.* **108,** Art. 2, 580 (1963).

chapter five

Composition of the Primordial Atmosphere

The catastrophe theory of the origin of the solar system pronounced by Sir James Jeans, ran into more and more conflict with subsequent cosmological discoveries. In 1952 Urey proposed a theory of the origin of the planets which is in conformity with the growing belief of many astronomers in a "steady-state universe." According to this view, the over-all composition of the universe does not change. Stars, planetary systems, and galaxies continuously form, develop, and die out, returning to the universe matter which forms the basis for the development of new stars and systems. The material from which this generation and regeneration occurs is in interstellar space in the form of gas and dust. By far the most abundant substance in the interstellar material is hydrogen which comprises more than 90 per cent of its mass.

Interstellar space is highly rarified, which is another way of saying that the density of its gas and dust is extremely low. In addition to hydrogen, only helium and neon exist as gases in the near-absolute zero temperature of interstellar space. Other substances exist in the solid state in the form of small particles, and these constitute the dust phase. The particles consist of elements and their compounds—oxides, sulfides, carbides, silicates, etc. Water is present in the form of ice crystals and combined as water of crystallization of various minerals. Methane and ammonia, also in the frozen state, contribute to the dust phase.

Large irregular dark blotches can be seen against the luminous background of our galaxy—the Milky Way. These are clouds of gas and dust that are opaque to light and thus blot out the stars beyond them (Fig. 5-1). They may have an expanse of 600–700 light-years, or about 4×10^{15} miles. Some idea of their diffuseness can be gained from the fact that a cloud of these dimensions, if compressed to the density of the sun, would have a diameter of only 4×10^6 miles—one billionth of its original expanse. Smaller, denser gas and dust clouds are also present but usually in the form of globules which appear as circular black spots against the starry sky. The globular clouds are probably the immediate source for the formation of new stars and systems.

Fig. 5-1. Dust and Gas Clouds in the Milky Way. The irregular dark patches are the clouds of dust and gas that obstruct the light from stars lying beyond. Photograph from the Mount Wilson and Palomar Observatories.

Urey proposed that the solar system originated from such a globule 1 light-year in diameter and at a temperature greatly below 0°C. A large portion of this globule began condensing rapidly into a compact mass. The great heat and enormous pressure resulting from this condensation initiated thermonuclear reactions that converted the mass into a luminous body—the sun.

After the sun was formed, the remainder of the gas and dust cloud was constrained by the resulting gravitational field into a flattened, unstable disc at the present plane of the ecliptic. The temperature of the disc varied according to the distance from the sun much as the temperatures of the present planets vary. In other words, the portion of the disc of dust and gas nearest to the sun rose rapidly and considerably in temperature, while the remotest edge of the disc was but little elevated in temperature. The unstable disc fragmented into masses of various sizes; these were the "protoplanets" of the present planets. In each protoplanet, a process of condensation began, which in principle was the same for all. As the temperature rose due to the sun's radiation, substances with the corresponding melting point liquefied and thus facilitated agglomeration of particles into larger bodies, the planetesimals. In this way, each planet had its beginning.

At this phase, the temperature of the protoplanet earth was about what it is now through the effect of solar radiation. While the mass was condensing, all substances in a gaseous state escaped from the vicinity of the protoplanet, which as yet was too small to hold gases by gravitational field. The elements and compounds that are normally gases at the temperature of the earth were retained by the protoplanet only if these gases were in chemical combination as nonvolatile substances, for example, nitrogen as metal nitrides, oxygen as oxides, hydrogen as water of hydration of minerals, etc. Thus, the young planet earth had no atmosphere of gases. An atmosphere of secondary origin was accumulated at a later stage.

Considerable heat was generated by the release of gravitational energy during the condensation of the dust. If this occurred sufficiently rapidly, heat would accumulate faster than radiation from the surface could dissipate it. Radioactive decay of Th, U, and K^{40} would add significantly to the accumulation of heat. At temperatures of 1000–3000°C, melting of various substances would take place. A stratification would occur, in which the heavier molten metals, for example, iron and nickel, would migrate to the core. Graphite and iron would form iron carbide at about 3000°C. The lighter substances would "float" to the surface of the molten mass, there to cool and to add to the crust. In this layer are found the hydrated minerals, basalt and granite. Heat loss by radiation reduced the surface temperature to what it is now, soon after the earth completed its growth.

Early Earth Atmosphere

According to one view, the average temperature of the earth's surface has been about what it is now since its earliest beginnings. The present surface temperature is maintained almost exclusively by radiation from the sun. In the absence of a screening layer of ozone in the upper atmosphere, as now exists, short-wave ultraviolet reached the surface. This range of ultraviolet, 2000 Å and less, promotes many chemical changes. Water absorbs in this range and the resulting oxygen of the reaction

$$H_2O \xrightarrow{h\nu} H_2 + \tfrac{1}{2}O_2$$

could not accumulate because the oxygen was avidly picked up by a variety of reduced substances, which formed the corresponding oxides. This process was facilitated by the escape of the lighter gas, hydrogen. In the early growth phase of the earth, meteorites containing iron and water on striking the earth would generate enough heat to cause the formation of iron oxide and hydrogen. Iron oxide and carbon react to form carbon monoxide and carbon dioxide. Carbon monoxide reacts with hydrogen to yield methane and other carbon-hydrogen compounds. As the earth grew in size, the escaping tendency of the gases was reduced more and more. At the present, the escape of hydrogen from the atmosphere into space is very low—about 10^{-9} gms/cm^2/yr—while that of other gases is practically nil. The metal carbides, nitrides, and sulfides yield hydrocarbons, ammonia, and hydrogen sulfide on reacting with water. Carbon dioxide in this early period readily formed carbonates of various kinds and thus, as in the case of oxygen, did not accumulate in the atmosphere. Consequently, the secondary atmosphere of the earth consisted of methane, water vapor, ammonia, and hydrogen. Small quantities of higher hydrocarbons, hydrogen sulfide, carbon monoxide, and nitrogen were probably also present.

In all its essential features Oparin's theory concerning the composition of the early atmosphere is in conformity with the foregoing theory of the origin of the solar system although he assumed a fiery origin of the earth.

The primordial atmosphere of the earth was different from the present one and had a markedly reducing character. Its content of ammonia, hydrogen sulfide, and later, hydrogen cyanide made it highly toxic for any known living organisms. This was a period of sterility but one of great productivity in organic chemical synthesis.

The theory that the early atmosphere contained carbon dioxide has been the basis of several hypotheses on the origin of life or of organic compounds. Haldane suggested that the abiogenic formation of organic compounds took place by the action of ultraviolet light on water, carbon dioxide, and ammonia. Calvin's group,[1] using the ionizing radiations from a cyclotron at a target of carbon dioxide and water, succeeded in synthesizing formic acid, formaldehyde, oxalic acid, and acetic acid. In this experiment carbon dioxide was reduced, and carbon-carbon bonds were formed. The yield, however, in terms of energy consumption was very small. It must be borne in mind, though, that the lithosphere originally had a much greater amount of radioactive elements than now and that the ionizing radiation from this source (U^{235}, Th, K^{40}, etc.) could contribute to the over-all organic synthesis as proposed by Calvin. However, only the carbon dioxide of the atmosphere within effective range of the emanations would be activated.

More recently others have also proposed a carbon dioxide-containing primitive atmosphere. Sokolov[2] assumed that the greater part of the earth's crust was affected by alpha-particles, which could be responsible for the formation of considerable amounts of oxygen by bombarding such oxides as SiO_2, Al_2O_3, H_2O, and Fe_2O_3 in the lithosphere. The oxygen, he maintained, would form a variety of gaseous oxides of the elements carbon, sulfur, and nitrogen. All of these gases except carbon monoxide and carbon dioxide would enter various reactions; the carbon monoxide and carbon dioxide would be given off into the atmosphere where, reacting with hydrogen, they would give rise to a certain quantity of hydrocarbons.

Other workers base their belief on geochemical grounds that carbon dioxide was the main carbon source in the primordial atmosphere for the synthesis of organic compounds. Outgassing of the earth and emissions from volcanoes, fumaroles, etc., add carbon dioxide and carbon monoxide to the atmosphere. It can be safely assumed that such processes occurred on a much larger scale in the remote past than now.

Bernal[3] also considers carbon dioxide rather than methane as the carbon source in the primitive atmosphere for the abiogenic synthesis of organic compounds. In part, this preference is based on geochemical grounds, but more so on his adherence to "the principle of Lyell which tells us to search in the present world for processes which may have occurred in the past." Bernal observes that in applying this principle to the origin of life, we are "to search in the inorganic world for the origin of the processes as well as the materials of the organic world," and "that the major features of current metabolism were already present in the primitive atmosphere. . . ." At best, this view can be taken as a working hypothesis, but surely not as a certainty. Bernal also believes that the compounds which make up organisms "can be most easily envisaged as constructed mainly of carbon dioxide and ammonia by not implausible processes which do not involve unsupported hypotheses about the constitution of the primitive atmosphere." The plausibility of a compound serving as a carbon source for organic synthesis can be tested by appropriate experimentation. A number of such experiments, pre- and post-1953,* can be cited, and they generally point to a more reduced form of carbon than carbon dioxide, for example, carbon monoxide and methane, as being more effective in the production of organic compounds. Carbon dioxide, however, may serve as a source of organic compounds in an appropriate *reducing* mixture of gases. This will be discussed in the next chapter.

Theories concerning the composition of the primitive atmosphere were based on general assumptions and broad principles—cosmological and geochemical. However, in 1959, Miller and Urey[4] subjected the problem to a more rigorous examination. They assumed that the primitive atmosphere lasted long enough to permit the components to come to chemical equilibrium. From a consideration of the thermodynamic properties of possible components of an atmosphere, they concluded that the main carbon compound

*For the significance of this date, see Chapter 6.

of the atmosphere would have been methane as long as hydrogen was present at a pressure greater than 10^{-6} atm, that ammonia would largely have been dissolved in the oceans as NH_4^+ at pH 8 and a partial pressure of hydrogen not less than 10^{-5} atm, and that nitrogen would be in the atmosphere in moderate amounts. Water vapor would also be present. Other gases like hydrogen sulfide might also have been there in trace amounts. Oparin's postulated primitive atmosphere approximates this composition.

References

1. Garrison, W. M., Morrison, D. C., Hamilton, J. G., Benson, A. A., Calvin, M., *Science* **114,** 416 (1951).
2. Sokolov, V. A., in Oparin, A. I., ed., "The Origin of Life on the Earth" (I. U. B. Sympos. Series, Vol. 1), Pergamon Press, New York, 1959, p. 54.
3. Bernal, J. D., in Oparin, A. I., ed., "The Origin of Life on the Earth" (I. U. B. Sympos. Series, Vol. 1), Pergamon Press, New York, 1959, p. 38.
4. Miller, S. L., and Urey, H. C., *Science* **130,** 245 (1959).

chapter six

Primary Synthesis of Organic Compounds

The turning point in the experimental approach to the problem of the origin of life came in 1953. In that year S. L. Miller[1] reported the results of his now classical experiments on the synthesis of organic compounds from a reducing mixture of simple gases. With the results of these experiments before it, the scientific community could seriously entertain the possibility of the origin of life from inorganic beginnings. The long era of speculations and fumbling was over, and lines of further experimentation suggested themselves. Attention was sharply focussed on Oparin's theory of the origin of life. His most important deduction, and the one originally most difficult to accept, had been vindicated: the feasibility of the abiogenic synthesis of organic compounds from methane, ammonia, hydrogen, and water vapor. Important, too, is that many of the organic compounds thus formed are biochemically significant. The rest of Oparin's hypothesis flows logically from this step, and now that it turned out to be possible his whole theory was given wide and thorough attention. Almost immediately, reports of experiments bearing on a number of different aspects of the problem began to appear. The theory has diverged into new avenues, all being vigorously followed. Differences of opinion have arisen, welcome and encouraging, although sometimes acrimonious. This scientifically exciting climate prevails today, and probably will continue for a long time with a correspondingly large outpouring of significant results.

Organic Synthesis from Gas Mixtures

Miller's apparatus (Fig. 6-1), with which he started this chain of events, is simple enough. In it, methane, ammonia, and hydrogen circulate past electrical discharges from tungsten electrodes. Steam from boiling water in the small flask mixes with the other gases in the large chamber. The mixture is energized by a continuous sparking across the electrodes from a high frequency Tesla coil. The steam condenses to water in the condenser and flows back into the flask of boiling water, at the same time bringing down some of the less volatile products. The U-tube at the base of the apparatus traps liquids and thus promotes circulation in one direction. The

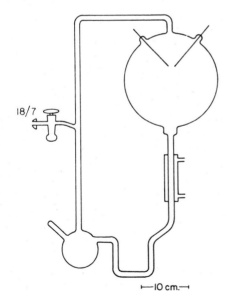

Fig. 6-1. Spark - discharge Apparatus. From Miller, S. L., *J. Am. Chem. Soc.* **77**, 2351, (1955).

experiment was run continuously for one week, analyses being conducted on the fluid in the small flask. Tentatively, glycine, alanine, β-alanine, aspartic acid and α-amino-n-butyric acid were identified. A yellow organic polymer had also formed, and its composition was reported later, as well as other findings.[2-4]

A truly amazing number and variety of organic compounds were formed from the simple starting materials by this ingenious method. Table 6-1 lists the results of a sample analysis. Purines and pyrimidines were notably absent. The silent discharge noted in column 3 of Table 6-1 was produced by an ozonizer. The products formed were similar, but the

TABLE 6-1 Yields of Compounds (Moles $\times$ 10^5)

	Spark Run 1	Silent Discharge Run 3	N_2 Run Run 6
Glycine	63 (2.1)*	80 (0.46)*	14.2 (0.48)*
Alanine	34	9	1.0
Sarcosine	5	86	1.5
β-Alanine	15	4	7.0
α-Aminobutyric acid	5	1	—
N-Methylalanine	1	12.5	—
Aspartic acid	0.4	0.2	0.3
Glutamic acid	0.6	0.5	0.5
Iminodiacetic acid	5.5	0.3	3.9
Imino-acetic-propionic acid	1.5	—	—
Formic acid	233	149	135
Acetic acid	15.2	135	41
Propionic acid	12.6	19	22
Glycolic acid	56	28	32
Lactic acid	31	4.3	1.5
α-Hydroxybutyric acid	5	1	—
Succinic acid	3.8	—	2
Urea	2	—	2
Methylurea	1.5	—	0.5
Sum of yields of compounds listed	15%	3%	8%

*Per cent yield of glycine, based on carbon placed in the apparatus as methane.

Miller, S. L., in Oparin, A. I., ed., "The Origin of Life on the Earth" (I.U.B. Sympos. Series), Pergamon Press, New York, 1959.

yield was quantitatively smaller than with sparking. Carbon monoxide, carbon dioxide, and nitrogen were also formed but are not included in the table.

Microbial synthesis could be ruled out on various grounds, and Miller unequivocally settled the question of contamination in two ways. The apparatus was prepared and run as usual but without sparking; yields were negligible. It was also prepared and first sterilized for 18 hrs at 130°C and then sparked; the yields were the same as in experiments run without autoclaving.

Sample analyses during the course of the experiment revealed that the concentration of ammonia dropped steadily. Hydrogen cyanide was synthesized early, within 24 hrs reaching a peak that was maintained for 110 hrs and then declined rapidly. Total aldehydes followed a similar course, but reached a lower peak. Total amino acids increased steadily for about five days and leveled off at a concentration of about $5 \times 10^{-3} M$ (Fig. 6-2).

The Miller experiment dramatically demonstrated the possibility of the abiogenic synthesis of abundant amounts of a variety of organic compounds from a reducing mixture of simple gases in which the only carbon source was methane. The probable origin and universal distribution of methane had already been elucidated by Urey[5]. The metaphysical aura surrounding the problem of the origin of life was thus lifted; serious discussion and experimentation could be, and was, undertaken. Reports on various phases of the problem continue to come from laboratories all over the world.

The results were confirmed in repeated experiments by Miller. Others have also corroborated the findings in general by this and other methods. [6-13] Among the experiments reported are those which differed from the Miller experiments either in starting material or energy source or both. Compounds other than methane for the carbon source, carbon

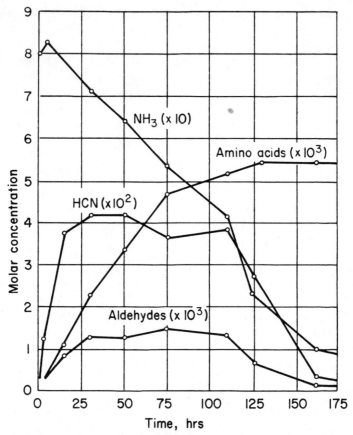

Fig. 6-2. Concentrations of Ammonia, Hydrogen cyanide, and Aldehydes in the U-tube, and Amino acids in the 500-ml Flask while Sparking a Mixture of Methane, Ammonia, Water, and Hydrogen in the Apparatus of Fig. 6-1. From Miller, S. L., *Biochim. Biophys. Acta* **23**, 484 (1957).

dioxide, carbon monoxide, formaldehyde, paraformaldehyde, formhydroxamic acid, glycol, and other mono- and dicarbon compounds have been used successfully by various workers.

However, reducing conditions must prevail when either carbon dioxide or carbon monoxide is used. Various energy sources have also been employed: heat, visible light, ultraviolet rays, X-rays, ionizing radiation, electric sparking, silent discharges, ultrasonic vibration, and hypersonics.

Abelson[8] tested carbon dioxide, carbon monoxide, and methane as the carbon source in the gas mixture of Miller-type experiments. For a nitrogen source he used ammonia and nitrogen. The effect of the presence of oxygen was also tested. His results confirmed the reducing atmosphere hypothesis. All three carbon sources were effective so long as the reaction mixture was reducing. Significant organic synthesis did not take place in an oxidizing mixture.

The effect of the presence of hydrogen sulfide in the reaction mixture was tested by Heyns, Walter, and Meyer.[9] The other gases in the mixture were methane, ammonia, and water vapor. Sulfur-containing compounds were recovered in addition to the usual yield. These were thiourea (thiocarbamide, NH_2CSNH_2), thioacetamide (CH_3CSNH_2), and thiocyanate ($CNSH$).

Pavlovskaya and Pasynskii[11] conducted experiments utilizing sparking on gas mixtures and ultraviolet rays on solutions. In their electric spark experiments, they used a modification of the Miller apparatus. They considered the thermodynamics of the over-all reactions in the synthesis of amino acids and calculated the free energy change for the formation of alanine as an example:

$$2H_2O + 3CH_4 + NH_3 \longrightarrow CH_3CH(NH_2)COOH + 6H_2$$
$$\Delta F = 62,040 \ cal/mole$$

Even without hydrogen among the reactants, 6 moles of hydrogen are formed according to the equation. The authors argue also that a more favorable energy relationship would be established by eliminating hydrogen in the reaction mixture and substituting carbon monoxide for it:

$$CH_4 + 2CO + NH_3 \longrightarrow CH_3CH(NH_2)COOH$$
$$\Delta F = -5900 \text{ cal/mole}$$

In their experiments with this gas mixture they recovered glycine, alanine, β-alanine, aspartic, glutamic, and α-amino-butyric acids, and lysine. Miller also reports all these except lysine. It is clear from the Pavlovskaya and Pasynskii experiment that amino acids can form in the absence of hydrogen if the reaction mixture is reducing in character. It must be added, however, that the reaction mechanisms are complex and twofold, those occurring in the spark phase and those occurring in the aqueous phase. Energy calculations based on the over-all reaction may not give a true picture.

The thermal synthesis of amino acids from methane, ammonia, and water was recently reported by Harada and Fox.[13] They passed the gases through a silica tube heated to 900–1000°C and obtained fourteen amino acids, all of which were of the naturally occurring α-amino variety. Other methods generally yield some amino acids not found in nature.

Anhydrous Organic Synthesis

Fox[17] synthesized amino acids by heating ammonium salts of Krebs cycle acids:

Ammonium malate $\xrightarrow[\text{3 hrs}]{200°C}$ peptide polymer $\xrightarrow[\text{hydrolysis}]{}$

aspartic acid + alanine

The same result, but with a lower yield, was obtained with ammonium fumarate. Ammonium citrate and ammonium succinate gave negative results. It is interesting that the thermal conditions of amino acid formation are also those of polymerization. Very little free acid was found after 3 hrs of heating. The amino acids were identified after the polymer was hydrolyzed. It must be noted that starting with the ammonium salt of only one compound a polymer containing at least two and possibly more amino acids was formed. Fox and his co-workers have had a large measure of success in conducting thermal syntheses under anhydrous conditions.[17,18,32-34] His contention is that most syntheses, condensations, and polymerizations not only involve the formation of water from the reactants, but would proceed with great difficulty in the presence of water.

Organic Synthesis in Aqueous Medium

Amino acids and other organic compounds may have been synthesized in the early oceans from simple compounds. Experimentally, amino acids have been synthesized from formaldehyde and other C_1 as well as C_2 compounds in water. Some of the experiments of Baly, *et al.*,[15] in 1922 used as starting materials formhydroxamic acid, and formaldehyde in solution. Under the influence of light the formation of large numbers of organic compounds was reported. From a present-day background, this synthesis would seem to be feasible, but at that time it could not be repeated by other investigators. In 1934 Dhar and Mukherjee,[16] using glycol and other C_2 sources with nitrate and titanium oxide, reported the synthesis of amino acids.

Bahadur[6] reported the synthesis of a number of amino acids when paraformaldehyde, potassium nitrate or ammonia, and ferric chloride were exposed to strong sunlight. As the reaction progressed, some earlier amino acids disappeared and new ones appeared. This would indicate that, if a steady-state system could be established, all amino acids would continue to be present. Those amino acids that serve as the basis for the synthesis of other amino acids would be replenished from precursor substances in the medium. Even more startling is his report[7] of successful amino acid synthesis from paraformaldehyde, colloidal molybdenum oxide, and water exposed to the light of a 500 watt electric bulb for 25 days. This is remarkable, since the only source of nitrogen in this mixture was atmospheric nitrogen and since the high energy radiation that would appear to be necessary for these reactions was not present. Presumably atmospheric oxygen also was available so that the mixture must have been an oxidizing one. Bahadur concludes that not only were amino acids synthesized abiogenically in the primitive atmosphere from carbon dioxide, water, and atmospheric nitrogen with sunlight but also that this is still going on since these same conditions prevail. His suggested mechanism is that of light causing the "formation of certain free radicals that help in the subsequent synthesis of amino acids."

In their radiation experiments Pavlovskaya and Pasynskii[11] exposed solutions of formaldehyde and either ammonium nitrate or ammonium chloride to ultraviolet rays. When ammonium chloride was the source of nitrogen, a good yield of amino acids was obtained at 40–45°C in a distinctly acid medium. When ammonium nitrate was the nitrogen source, the yield was best at 1–2°C. Among the amino acids obtained by this method the authors list glycine, alanine, serine, valine, glutamic acid, phenylalanine, isoleucine, and basic amino acids.

Oró and his group[19] in 1959 synthesized the amino acids glycine, alanine, β-alanine, serine, threonine, and aspartic acid. Formic, glycolic, and lactic acids also were reported. Sugar was indicated, but not definitely identified. These syntheses were brought about by heating solutions of formaldehyde and hydroxylamine to 70–100°C. Oró and Kamat[20] obtained traces of glycine, alanine, and aspartic acid by heating $3N$ aqueous ammonia saturated with hydrogen cyanide at 70°C for 25 days.

In 1963 Lowe, Rees, and Markham[21] synthesized a very

great number of organic compounds by heating liquid hydrogen cyanide and aqueous ammonia at 90°C for 18 hrs. Some polymers were also formed. These were hydrolyzed, and the hydrolysate was analyzed along with the free monomers. Nine amino acids were definitely identified; another five remained unidentified. β-Alanine, α,β-diaminopropionic acid, and α-aminobutyric acid were also identified. In all, 75 ninhydrin-reacting and 50 non-ninhydrin-reacting compounds were formed, but not all were identified.

Other Simple Organic Compounds

Some biochemically important compounds are missing from the products reported in the previous experiments. These are the hexoses, pentoses, purines, and pyrimidines. The hexose glucose serves as the main source of energy in metabolism. The great importance of the pentoses derives from the role ribose and 2-deoxyribose play in the formation of nucleotides and nucleic acids. Recent reports of the abiogenic synthesis of some of these compounds under possible primitive earth conditions is therefore highly significant.

Polyhydroxyaldehydes, not specifically identified, have been detected by a number of investigators among the products formed in experiments on the synthesis of amino acids. The sugars are probably included among these. In 1962 Oró and Cox[22] synthesized 2-deoxyribose by the condensation of formaldehyde and acetaldehyde or acetaldehyde and glyceraldehyde in aqueous salt solutions. Ribose and deoxyribose were synthesized by Ponnamperuma and Mariner[23] in 1963, by the irradiation of dilute solutions of formaldehyde with ultraviolet or gamma rays.

Purines, Pyrimidines, and Their Derivatives

Living things today cannot do without purine and pyrimidine derivatives. Adenine, guanine, xanthine, hypoxanthine, and uric acid are biologically important purine derivatives. Uracil, thymine, and cytosine are some of the biologically important pyrimidine derivatives. These derivatives combined with ribose or deoxyribose, and phosphate, form the corresponding nucleotides. Some nucleotides function as such in the metabolism of the cell. Nucleotides are also the structural units of the nucleic acids, ribonucleic acid (RNA), and deoxyribonucleic acid (DNA). As the names imply, the sugars are ribose and 2-deoxyribose, respectively. Adenylic acid, a purine nucleotide, and uridylic acid, a pyrimidine nucleotide, are shown in Fig. 6–3. The nucleotides polymerize into long chains, the nucleic acids, in which the coupling is through phosphate linked to the 3' carbon of the pentose of one nucleotide and the 5' carbon of the pentose of the next nucleotide. DNA embodies the codes which determine amino acid sequences, and thus the biochemical properties, of proteins most of which are enzymes. DNA is thought to be the essential component of genes and therefore is identified with the mechanism of inheritance of living things. RNA is of many kinds which function in receiving the codes from DNA, in transferring the codes to the site of protein synthesis, in the activation of amino acids, and in the transfer of amino acids to the site of protein synthesis.

If the nucleotides had even a few of the roles in the first organisms that they play in the metabolism of present organisms, the demonstration of the synthesis of purines, pyrimidines, nucleotides, and nucleic acids under possible primitive earth conditions would be indispensible to our understanding of the mechanism of the origin of life. Recent reports of success along these lines have been very encouraging.

Synthesis of Purines, Pyrimidines, and Their Derivatives

Interestingly enough, adenine was the first of the nitrogenous bases to be synthesized under possible primitive earth

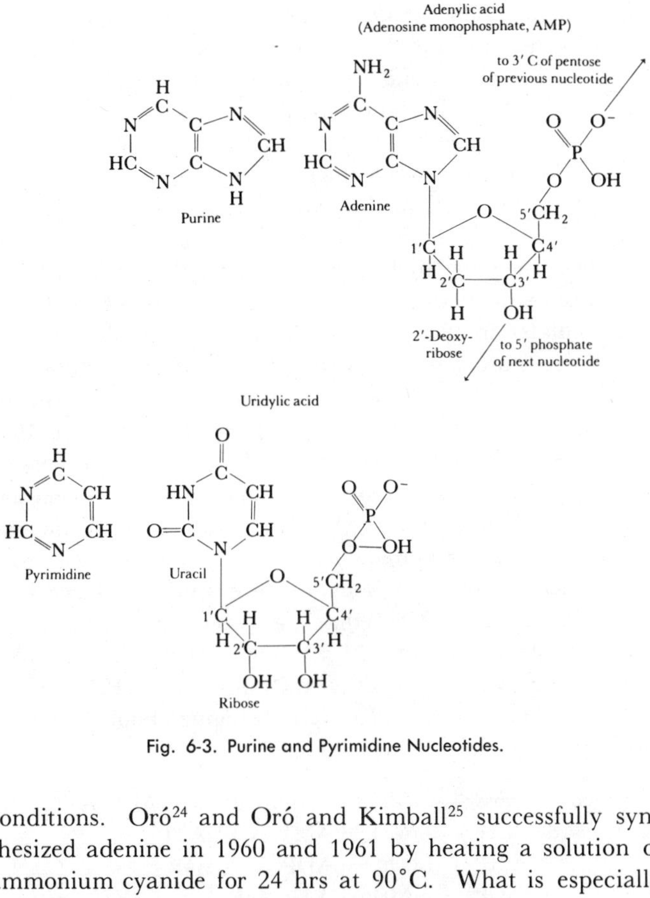

Fig. 6-3. Purine and Pyrimidine Nucleotides.

conditions. Oró[24] and Oró and Kimball[25] successfully synthesized adenine in 1960 and 1961 by heating a solution of ammonium cyanide for 24 hrs at 90°C. What is especially interesting about this synthesis is the formation, also, of 5-aminoimidazole-4-carboximide, which is an intermediate compound in the biological synthesis of adenine. At an early stage in the biosynthesis of adenine, glycine takes part, and this amino acid was also found among the products. Adenine is one of the most important of the nitrogenous bases. As adenosine monophosphate (AMP), diphosphate (ADP), and triphosphate (ATP) it takes part in many types of metabolic reactions and also is one of the bases in the structure of both RNA and DNA. Its synthesis under primitive earth conditions lends support to theories on the origin of life which assume the pre-existence of nucleic acids.

Close on the heels of this announcement came the report from Fox and Harada[26] of the synthesis of uracil, a pyrimidine, from methane, hydrogen, and water, also under possible primitive earth conditions. Acetic acid and malic acid were intermediates in this synthesis. Malic acid, reacting with urea, formed uracil with polyphosphoric acid as a catalyst.

Lowe and his colleagues,[21] mentioned earlier, synthesized the bases adenine, guanine, and hypoxanthine. In 1963 Ponnamperuma and his co-workers[27-30] reported in a series of experiments the synthesis of adenine, guanine, adenosine, and the nucleotides AMP, ADP, and ATP. During thermal copolymerization of amino acids, guanine was also formed.[27] Ultraviolet rays on 10^{-4} M hydrogen cyanide produced both adenine and guanine.[28] Methane, ammonia, and water under the effect of electrons at 5 Mev formed adenine but no other purine or pyrimidine.[29] Ethyl metaphosphate (EtMtP) was found to be particularly effective in bringing about the formation of nucleosides and nucleotides:[30]

Adenine + ribose + EtMtP→ adenosine, AMP, ADP, ATP, A4P
Adenosine + EtMtP→ AMP, ADP, ATP
AMP + EtMtP→ ADP, ATP, A4P
ADP + EtMtP→ ATP, A4P

(AMP is adenosine monophosphate; ADP, adenosine diphosphate; ATP, adenosine triphosphate; and A4P, adenosine tetraphosphate.)

Schramm and his colleagues[31] in 1962 had reported a similar catalytic effect of complex polyphosphate esters, $\widetilde{P}$, on a number of polymerization reactions. Nucleoside and nucleotide formation was mediated by those esters:

$$\text{Ribose} + \text{adenine} \xrightarrow{\tilde{P}} \text{adenosine} + 2',3'\text{-diphosphoadenosine}$$

$$\text{Deoxyribose} + \text{adenine} \xrightarrow{\tilde{P}} \text{deoxyadenosine}$$

Synthesis of Macromolecules

The macromolecules that have received the most attention in relation to the question of the origin of life are the proteins and nucleic acids. The abiogenic synthesis of macromolecules on the primitive earth is more speculative than is the synthesis of simpler organic compounds. This is only natural. There are fewer complications encountered in the synthesis of small molecules; relatively simple experiments can be designed to bring evidence to bear on any of the proposed theories. Also, a long history of organic chemical synthesis in the laboratory can be related to the subject. However, attempts to synthesize protein without enzyme mediation have failed until recently; only peptides which did not resemble proteins were formed. It has even been questioned whether the first living things were necessarily protein- or nucleic acid-dependent. In spite of these questions, it would be highly important to have some demonstration that proteins and nucleic acids can arise abiogenically under presumed primitive earth conditions.

Polypeptide and Protein Synthesis

Peptide bond formation has been accomplished since the beginning of this century in a variety of ways. In 1902 Emil Fischer suggested that proteins are formed by amide linkage between adjacent amino acid residues. This is brought about by the joining of the α-amino group of one amino acid to the α-carboxyl group of the adjacent amino acid with the elimination of a molecule of water for every such union. This hypothesis (independently advanced in the same year by F. Hofmeister) inspired experimentation on peptide synthesis to which Fischer contributed. But most of the techniques and substances employed were not feasible under primitive earth conditions, and the results were not at all like proteins. At the present, three interesting lines of attack have been tried, and all seem to be compatible with presumed primitive earth conditions. These are as follows: (1) The synthesis of amino acids and the simultaneous polymerization of these to high molecular weight protein-like substances, (2) the end-to-end linkage of activated amino acids into long peptide chains, and (3) the formation of polyglycine chains of appreciable length and the subsequent modification of the chain by inserting at appropriate sites various side chains which are characteristic of naturally occurring amino acids. In this fashion the homo-polymer, polyglycine, is converted to the heteropolymeric structure found in proteins.

The first line of attack has been followed very successfully by Fox and his colleagues.[17,18,32-34] The method consists, essentially, of heating a mixture of amino acids under anhy-drous conditions to temperatures of $160-200°C$ for periods of $\frac{1}{2}-3$ hrs. At first, in 1955, ammonium salts of Krebs cycle acids were heated individually with varying success. Later they reported the synthesis of a linear peptide when glutamic acid was heated with any of a number of other amino acids. This technique was modified in 1958 to make a copolymer of the 18 amino acids found in proteins. Various copolymers had molecular weights from 3000 to 9000, depending on the method of preparation, and all were remarkably similar to natural proteins. The major differences were molecular weight (the copolymers were at the lower range of the molec-ular weights of natural proteins), lack of antigenicity (they did not stimulate the production of antibodies when injected into rabbits), and optical activity (some racemization of reactant amino acids took place during synthesis). Due to their great resemblance to proteins in most ways, Fox named these copolymers "proteinoids." A great excess of glutamic and aspartic acids is required for the formation of proteinoids. The ratio of glutamic acid to aspartic acid to 16 other amino acids combined was 2:2:1. The details of the preparation and the characteristics of the proteinoids were described in 1960.[18] Thermal copolymerization was also reported in 1963 by Ponnamperuma.[14] The several polymers that were formed in the experiments by Lowe, Rees, and Markham[21] probably also contained peptide chains. Both of the last cited experiments began with simple reactants that did not include amino acids and that resulted in the formation of numerous products among which were amino acid polymers, possibly following the same pattern as the experiments of Fox. It seems then that one and the same set of conditions gives rise to amino acids and brings about their polymerization.

In the second line of attack, end-to-end reaction of amino acids requires that the participating amino acids be activated at the reacting group. Becker and Stahmann[35] found that N-carboxyamino acid anhydrides polymerize readily into peptide structures. Schramm and Wissmann[36] and Schramm, Groetsch, and Pullman[31] activated the carboxyl group of tripeptides with a polyphosphate ester. With mild treatment, which did not cause loss of optical activity, tripeptide esters, for example, alanylglycylglycine phosphate, easily polymerized into polypeptides of 24–40 amino acid residues. By heating amino acid amides, Oró and Guidry[37] brought about polycondensations of amino acids in an alkaline medium at $100°C$.

The third line of attack makes use of the fact that the backbone of protein molecules is a polyglycine peptide chain:

$$^+NH_3\dot{C}HCONH\dot{C}HCONH\ldots\dot{C}HCOO^-$$

The proteins differ from each other in a number of ways, one of which is in the types of side chains found at the —ĊH— groups. It is therefore theoretically possible to synthesize a protein by insertion of appropriate side chains at the —ĊH— groups of a previously synthesized polyglycine. Oró and Guidry[37,40] described the direct polycondensation of amino acid amides and synthesis of a polyglycine containing eighteen glycine residues. In 1956 Akabori, Okawa, and Sato[38] introduced serine and threonine into polyglycine to obtain a variegated protein, and in 1959 Akabori[39] discussed the details of the theory of the "fore-protein" and its possible origin in prebiological times. Kliss and Matthews[41] advanced an intriguing hypothesis on the formation of polyglycines and their conversion into protein, the formation also of polysaccharides, nitrogenous bases, nucleotides, and possibly nucleic acids, all from activated hydrogen cyanide and hydrogen cyanide dimers. These last two theoretical treatments will be taken up in the section on reaction mechanisms (Chapter 7).

Synthesis of Nucleic Acids

The synthesis of high molecular weight nucleic acids, using conditions compatible with those presumed to exist in pre-biological times, has been an elusive problem. Recently Schramm and co-workers[31] described a successful method starting with nucleotides rather than nucleotide phosphates. High concentrations of nucleotides were mixed directly with a viscous polyphosphate ester of special formulation, and the mixture was allowed to rotate at 50–60°C. The special phosphate ester was made by dissolving phosphorus pentoxide in ether and other solvents containing alkoxyl groups. The resulting viscous polyphosphate ester is complex and its structure unknown. This technique yielded nucleic acids with molecular weights of 15,000–50,000 or 60–200 residues, whereas other methods yielded polynucleotides with only a few residues.

Synthesis of Polysaccharides

The polyphosphate ester technique has been applied by Schramm and his co-workers to the synthesis of polysaccharides also. The underlying principle is the activation of reacting units of the condensation process with polyphosphate. Their polyphosphate will form an ester linkage with, and thus activate, free hydroxyl, amino, or carbonyl groups. Activated sugars will polymerize readily to polysaccharides of fairly high molecular weights. Glucose-1-polyphosphate yields a polyglycoside with a molecular weight of 50,000; the ribose phosphate and fructose phosphate each give a corresponding polymer with a molecular weight of 40,000. Mora and Wood[42] also reported a high molecular weight polymer of glucose on heating a mixture of glucose and 0.164 per cent phosphoric acid to 140–170°C in a vacuum.

Thus, only a little more than a decade after Miller first established the feasibility of the synthesis of organic compounds from a simple gas mixture, an overwhelming amount of further evidence has emerged from laboratories in many parts of the world on the abiogenic synthesis of organic compounds under possible primitive earth conditions. The outlook is good also for the successful synthesis in the near future of all kinds of macromolecules under presumed prebiological conditions. We can anticipate the time when the existence of all manner of organic compounds on the primitive earth can be accepted as likely. As long as water and some form of nitrogen were present under reducing conditions, any one of the simple carbon compounds could have given rise to the whole gamut of organic substances. As long as some form of energy (heat, light, electric discharge, ultraviolet rays, X-rays, gamma rays of cosmic origin or from decay of radioactive elements, ultrasonic vibrations) was present in sufficient quantity, any or all could have served the purpose. Hypersonic chemosynthesis[43] is one of the latest additions to this impressive array of energy sources. Given all these manifold possibilities, the question is not if and how organic compounds could arise abiogenically, but rather how they could have failed to originate.

Discrete Systems

The transition from molecules to living systems is difficult to reconstruct. Of course, the intricacy of the construction will depend on the criteria of life to be satisfied. Living things, according to Madison's definition (Chapter 1) probably came into being even before the advent of macromolecules. In the chemically reactive milieu, when abiogenic organic chemical synthesis was taking place, it is conceivable that certain endergonic reactions were harmoniously correlated with exergonic reactions. This would satisfy Madison's definition.

Another definition of life easily satisfied is the Muller[44] or Horowitz[45] concept. According to Muller, the naked gene is the simplest form of life. It was possible to put this in chemical terms when DNA was identified as the most likely substance of the gene. Horowitz includes the environment in which the gene must operate as part of his definition of life: "Life arose as individual molecules (genes, DNA) in a polymolecular environment." (Chapter 1)

The presumed role of DNA in organisms today is to carry and perpetuate the codes for the synthesis of specific proteins. There are indications, however, that the abiogenic synthesis of proteins did not require the intervention of DNA. Indeed, the formation of isolated systems with a primitive metabolism incorporating proteins both as structural elements and participants also does not need the intervention of DNA. The arrival on the scene of DNA as a regulatory refinement would seem more logical after a protein-dependent primitive living thing came into being. The view that the primitive living system served as the selection medium for the appropriate nucleic acids seems more satisfactory than the one that the nucleic acids, by long chance, became assembled into the precise

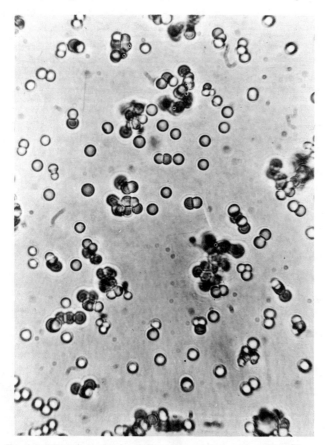

Fig. 6-4. Microspheres Produced from Thermal Protenoid. Microspheres of uniform size under low magnification. Courtesy Fox, S. W., Inst. for Space Biosciences, the Florida State University.

structure necessary to determine, all at once, an intricately balanced whole mechanism.

Oparin's coacervates still serve as the model of isolated metabolizing systems developing by degrees into the first primitive living things. Much work on coacervates has been done since 1936 by many different workers, including Oparin. Complex and multiple coacervates have been constructed, which incorporate enzyme as well as substrate, for example, α-amylase and starch. The rate of hydrolysis of the starch within the coacervate, however, is more variable there than in the medium. Apparently, coacervate structure can affect or moderate the action of enzymes. Even the complex coacervate systems which incorporate enzymes and substrates come eventually to a static equilibrium with the environment and so are far removed from the living state.

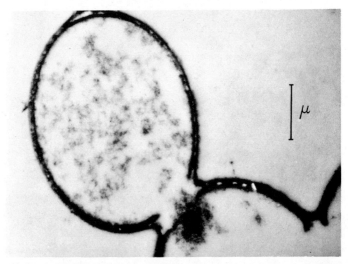

Fig. 6-5. Double-walled Membrane Is Shown in Electron Micrograph of Microsphere Produced from Thermal Protenoid. Courtesy Fox, S. W., Inst. for Space Biosciences, the Florida State University.

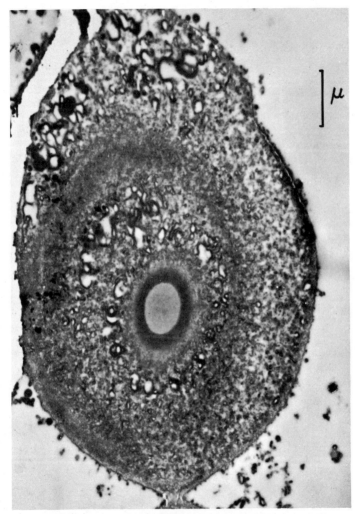

Fig. 6-6. Vacuolar Contents Are Shown in Electron Micrograph of Microsphere Produced from Thermal Protenoid. Courtesy Fox, S. W., Inst. for Space Biosciences, the Florida State University.

Another way in which life could have started in minute discrete particles, spontaneously separating from the environmental mixture of chemicals, has been proposed by Fox. The synthesis of proteinoids by Fox and his group has been mentioned. When proteinoid is treated with hot water, microspheres (Fig. 6-4) separate out of the cooling, clear solution.[46] Typical microspheres are 1–3 μ in diameter, but may be as large as 80 μ. They show osmotic and permeability phenomena and ATP-splitting activity. Typical microspheres are stable and can be sectioned and stained with various biological stains. Differential treatment can simulate some aspects of cells, for example, double-walled membranes (Fig. 6-5), vacuolar (Fig. 6-6) or granular internal differentiation, and variation in shape and cell division (Fig. 6-4). Microspheres, too, are far from the living state, the attainment of which presents problems similar to those of coacervates.

References

1. Miller, S. L., *Science* **117**, 528 (1953).
2. ———, *J. Am. Chem. Soc.* **77**, 2351 (1955).
3. ———, *Biochim. Biophys. Acta* **23**, 480 (1957).
4. ———, in Oparin, A. I., ed., "The Origin of Life on the Earth" (I. U. B. Sympos. Series, Vol. 1) Pergamon Press, New York, 1959, p. 123.
5. Urey, H. C., "The Planets," Yale University Press, New Haven, Conn. 1952.
6. Bahadur, K., *Nature* **173**, 1141 (1954).
7. ———, *et al.*, *Nature* **182**, 1668 (1958).
8. Abelson, P. H., *Science* **124**, 935 (1956).
9. Heyns, K., Walter, W., Meyer, E., *Naturwissenschaften* **44**, 385 (1957).
10. Oró, J., *et al.*, *Arch. Biochem. Biophys.* **84**, 115 (1959).
11. Pavlovskaya, T. E., and Pasynskii, A. G., in Oparin, A. I., ed., "The Origin of Life on the Earth" (I. U. B., Sympos, Series Vol. 1) 151, Pergamon Press, New York, 1959.

12. Oró, J., and Kamat, S. S., *Nature* **190,** 442 (1961).

13. Harada, K., and Fox, S. W., *Science* **143,** 384 (1964).

14. Ponnamperuma, C., Young, R. S., Munoz, E., *Federation Proc.* **22,** 479 (1963).

15. Baly, E. C. C., Heibron, I. M., and Hudson, D. P., *J. Chem. Soc.* **121,** 1078 (1922).

16. Dhar, N. R., and Mukherjee, S. K., *Nature* **134,** 499 (1934).

17. Fox, S. W., Johnson, J. E., and Middlebrook, M., *J. Am. Chem. Soc.* **77,** 1048 (1955).

18. Fox, S. W., and Harada, K., *J. Am. Chem. Soc.* **82,** 3745 (1960).

19. Oró, J., Kimball, A., Fritz, R., and Master, F., *Arch. Biochem. Biophys.* **85,** 115 (1959).

20. Oró, J., and Kamat, J. S., *Nature* **190,** 442 (1961).

21. Lowe, C. U., Rees, M. W., and Markham, R., *Nature* **199,** 219 (1963).

22. Oró, J., and Cox, A. C., *Federation Proc.* **25,** 80 (1962).

23. Ponnamperuma, C., Mariner, R., *Radiation Res.* **19,** 183 (1963).

24. Oró, J., *Biochem. Biophys. Res. Commun.* **2,** 407 (1960).

25. Oró, J., and Kimball, A. P., *Arch. Biochem. Biophys.* **94,** 217 (1961).

26. Fox, S. W., and Harada, K., *Science* **133,** 1923 (1961).

27. Ponnamperuma, C., Young, R. S., Munoz, E., *Federation Proc.* **22,** 479 (1963); *see* 14.

28. Ponnamperuma, C., and Mariner, R., *19th Proc. Intern. Congr. Pure Appl. Chem., London, 1963.*

29. Ponnamperuma, C., *et al., Proc. Nat. Acad. Sci. U. S.* **49,** 737 (1963).

30. Ponnamperuma, C., Sagan, C., and Mariner, R., *Nature* **199,** 222 (1963).

31. Schramm, G., Groetsch, H., and Pullman, W., *Angew. Chem., Intern. Ed. Engl.* **1,** 1 (1962).

32. Harada, K., Fox, S. W., *J. Am. Chem. Soc.* **80,** 2694 (1958).

33. Vegotsky, A., Fox, S. W., *Federation Proc.* **18,** 343 (1959).

34. Fox, S. W., and Harada, K., *Federation Proc.* **22,** 479 (1963).

35. Becker, R. R., Stahmann, A. M., *J. Biol. Chem.* **204,** 737 (1953).

36. Schramm, G., and Wissmann, H., *Chem. Ber.* **91,** 1073 (1958).

37. Oró, J., and Guidry, C. C., *Nature* **186,** 156 (1960).

6868686868 of life*

686868

6868686868. Akabori, S., Okawa, K., Sato, M., *Bull. Chem. Soc. Japan* **29**, 608 (1956).
39. Akabori, S., in Oparin, A. I., ed., "The Origin of Life on the Earth" (I. U. B. Sympos. Series, Vol. 1), Pergamon Press, New York, 1959, p. 189.
40. Oró, J., and Guidry, C. C., *Arch. Biochem. Biophys.* **93,** 166 (1961).
41. Kliss, R. M., and Matthews, C. N., *Proc. Natl. Acad. Sci. U. S.* **48,** 1300 (1962).
42. Mora, P. T., and Wood, J. W., *J. Am. Chem. Soc.* **80,** 685 (1958).
43. Hochstim, A. R., *Proc. Natl. Acad. Sci.* **50,** 200 (1963).
44. Muller, H. J. *Proc. 4th. Intern. Congr. Planned Sci., Ithaca, N. Y., 1926,* 897 (1929).
45. Horowitz, N. H., in Oparin, A. I., ed., "The Origin of Life on the Earth" (I. U. B. Sympos. Series, Vol. 1), Pergamon Press, New York, 1959, p. 106.
46. Fox, S. W. Harada, K., Kendrick, J., *Science* **129,** 1221 (1959).

chapter seven

Some Unsettled Questions

There are many aspects to the problem of the origin of life. Questions have arisen as each aspect has been subjected to experimentation or analysis. It can hardly be said that any of the questions has been settled with universal approval. But some questions have come under more discussion or dispute than others. Six of these questions will be considered briefly now. They are: "The hot dilute soup," asymmetric synthesis (origin of optical activity), the origin of petroleum, energy considerations, reaction mechanisms, and the origin of living things from discrete systems.

From Static Discrete Systems to Living Things

The demonstration of the transition of discrete systems into living things has to include the answers to some very intricate problems. Coacervates and microspheres, in spite of various refinements which have already been introduced in each case, are still a long way from the living state. They are both static structures. Left alone, such systems come to an equilibrium in which the status quo is maintained with no exchange of energy or materials with the environment. Neither Oparin for his coacervates nor Fox for his microspheres maintains that the simulated cell structures represent the living state. Both look to further refinements toward the eventual attainment of living things by experimental techniques.

The hurdles in this transition are formidable. Blum has stressed this point in his writings.[1-3] Even conceptually it is difficult to see how a system satisfying the minimum criteria for a living thing can arise by chance and, simultaneously, include a mechanism containing the suitable information for its own replication. At first glance it might appear that the gene (and therefore DNA, the probable composition of the gene) could fit the description. This view has been championed by Horowitz,[4] who lists as the minimum criteria for a living thing self-replication, mutability, and heterocatalysis. These are also the properties of the gene. Heterocatalysis "is the ability to *influence the environment* in such a way as to *insure a supply of the materials necessary for the perpetuation of the system*" (Horowitz's italics). It is difficult to see how such assurance can be had unless the environment in question is in the immediate vicinity of the gene and *distinct from the general environment* (my italics). A gene by itself (in vacuo, so to speak) is meaningless. It has meaning only in relation to the phenotype which it determines. If a gene was indeed the first expression of life, its minimum phenotype was the very nature of this restricted environment, which must be separate from the surrounding medium. Thus, part of the heterocatalytic function of the gene needs to be directed at securing and maintaining its own specific environment.

Replication and mutation present even greater difficulties. The over-all process of replication is endergonic.[2] While replication proceeds, some other mechanism, coordinated in time and space with it, is needed to make available the requisite energy. If all these conditions are to be met at the time of the first origin of life, we must imagine that a DNA structure was built up by chance, containing a specific sequence of nucleotides and possessing a capacity to determine the composition of a supporting environment and the machinery for self-replication. This amounts to postulating the "all at once" origin of a cell with "cytoplasm" and "nucleus."

The proteinoid microspheres present an encouraging prospect, but at present they are structurally closer to killed and fixed cells than to their living counterparts. Membranes of many different kinds, as well as the membranes of microspheres, show simple osmotic and permeability phenomena which are only superficially like those of living cells. Microspheres, however, have had a very short history. To be comparable to cells, they need to have other substances as well as proteinoid in their composition. Their reported ability to split ATP will be more significant if the energy liberated can be made to drive a "useful" endergonic reaction. To be more like living cells, their stability *should be based on an unstable structure maintained through the constant utilization of energy and materials*.

Precisely because coacervates are unstable structures susceptible to destruction by changing environmental conditions, they are attractive candidates for possible prebiological structures. The cell, too, is unstable and will break down with significant internal changes in pH, ionic concentration, etc. The solution to the problem of the instability of coacervates is not to construct them of more stable substances but rather to incorporate the proper types of coordinated reversible reactions whose response to environmental changes will produce the internal adjustments necessary to stabilize the whole structure. The over-all "sameness" by which a living cell is recognized is not due to a fixed structure. Almost every component fluctuates between permissible levels of concentration. The direction or the rate of reversible reactions may change, and other adjustments may take place which permit the cell to maintain its identity and operations in the face of changing environmental conditions. When discrete systems can be made to have this kind of dynamic steady state characteristic of open systems, they are on the way to being alive.

But this is just a beginning. Some of the reactions of the system must be directed toward the synthesis of more of its components. This must happen at a rate at least equal to the rate of breakdown. When synthesis happens at a faster rate, growth will take place. Division is a natural concomitant to growth, and this reintroduces the problem of replication. How does a system arise, along with the machinery for its own replication? Perhaps the answer lies in separating the two processes in time. Prebiological microspheres or coacervates (or both) could have formed and could have broken down under a variety of different conditions. The special composition of these subvital systems could have been responsible for new synthetic pathways leading to the formation of more complex products which could not be synthesized in the general environment. Such systems with a capacity for growth but without a mechanism for division are destined to swell and eventually burst, enriching the environment with their contents. Thus, older systems by contributing new products to the environment will exert an influence on the structure of newer systems and their pathways. It is in such a hierarchy of increasingly complex structures that nucleic acids could have originally been synthesized, reflecting the nature of the "metabolic" system from which they arose. This statement is merely intended to convey the idea of the possibility that there was established, first, a system of coordinated pathways which later served as the medium for the selection of the appropriate replicating mechanism.

Hot Dilute Soup

The first living things, according to Haldane and Oparin, were heterotrophic and arose in an environment rich in organic compounds. The first organisms, surrounded by a wide variety of ready-made organic compounds and not having to synthesize that which was already available, could have managed with a simple metabolism. Urey[5] estimates that the primitive oceans could easily have had a 10 per cent concentration of organic compounds. This figure has been questioned. Various authors have expressed the opinion that the concentration of organic substances never reached a level high enough to permit appreciable reactivity among the components. According to this view, high concentrations of organic compounds occurred only locally, and life could, therefore, arise only in such localities. An estimate based on more recent assumptions concerning the rate of abiogenic organic chemical synthesis allows a one per cent solution of organic compounds in the waters of the primitive earth.

Bernal does not believe that it is necessary to assume the presence of a high concentration of organic compounds in oceans as a prerequisite to the origin of living things.[6] He argues that small organic molecules can become adsorbed on estuarian clays where in the presence of catalysts the synthesis of macromolecules could have taken place quite rapidly. The macromolecules would then be desorbed. The process could continue in this way to increase greatly the amount of specific macromolecules in a relatively restricted area. Specific catalysts in the clays would have favored synthesis along particular lines, and thus a vast array of organic compounds would not be needed for the establishment of life. The first living things would have incorporated some of those same catalysts, and thus would have had a metabolism reflecting the prebiotic pathways of synthesis. An advantage of Bernal's hypothesis is the possibility of asymmetric synthesis within the clays, as will be brought out later, leading to a preponderance of one of a pair of enantiomorphs. The exclusive presence of L-amino acids and D-sugars in practically all forms of living things may thereby have a ready explanation.

A drawback to Bernal's hypothesis is to be noted. There is good reason to assume that the multiplication of the first living things was perhaps not only rapid, but even logarithmic; their being heterotrophic made necessary the presence of vast amounts of ready-made organic compounds.

Another objection has been voiced to the concept of oceans of hot dilute soup. It is held by some that such a composition and concentration of organic compounds would result in an indiscriminate interaction leading to the formation of tarry substances not useful to life. Some "tarry messes" are polymers, not necessarily nondescript, useless substances as the designation "tarry mess" connotes. However, the premise itself, that a tar will result, may be wrong. Concomitant physicochemical conditions may prevent the formation of tars. Fox stabilizes his amino acid mixtures with an excess of dicarboxylic acids, and the mixture when heated yields proteinoids and not tars.[7]

Asymmetric Synthesis

If a carbon atom has a different substituent at each of its four bonds, it is said to form an asymmetric center in the molecule and the compound in which it is located can exist in either of two mirror-image forms (enantiomorphic states). For example, the amino acid alanine can exist in the forms

L-Alanine   D-Alanine

in which the middle carbon atom is the asymmetric center and the $-NH_2$ and $-H$ are in mirror-image position to each other. As previously mentioned, one finds almost exclusively L- but not D-amino acids and D- but not L-sugars in living things. This is due to the fact that the enzymes mediating in these syntheses are themselves correspondingly asymmetric. In laboratory synthesis and also in nature when no asymmetric forces are involved, the configuration around an asymmetric atom is at random, and racemic mixtures (equal amounts of each enantiomorph) result. The central question, therefore, is: How did the asymmetry in living things come about in the first place?

The preponderance of one over the other enantiomorph in living things has been explained mainly along two lines.

Natural Asymmetric Forces. One line of explanation involves the search for some asymmetric force in nature under which the synthesis of one enantiomorph would be favored. It has been suggested that circularly polarized light, as that reflected from the moon, or plane polarized light, as that reflected from the sea, are such forces. But the excess in the direction of polarization in either case is very small. Circularly and plane polarized light and other natural "forces," such as left- or right-oriented crystal surfaces, asymmetric catalysts, etc., have been considered and discarded by Wald.[8] Oparin, however, puts much emphasis on the few cases of asymmetric synthesis by polarized light and asymmetric catalysts.[9] In Bernal's hypothesis of organic chemosynthesis on clays, the possible presence of dissymmetric catalysts or mineral surfaces in the clays could play a role in asymmetric synthesis.

Natta[10] obtained stereospecific polymerization with synthetic organometallic catalysts that exist in enantiomorphic pairs. Gabriel[11] calls attention to inclusion compounds, which are formed by some substances when they crystallize in such fashion as to enclose an internal space or cage with specific dimensions. "Guest" molecules of complementary configuration can become enclosed therein. The configuration of the cage of a host inclusion compound may accommodate one member of a pair of enantiomorphic substances but not the other. In this way physical resolution of a racemic mixture may take place. Chemical resolution of racemic mixtures has also been demonstrated.[12] Recently Harada[13] reported the nonenzymic synthesis of L-alanine, $[\alpha]_D^{27} = +13.99°$ (95 per cent optically active). The method was essentially a Strecker synthesis which is considered to be a possible method of abiogenic amino acid formation on the primitive earth. The mechanism of the synthesis has not been clarified as yet.

Resolution by Competition Among Organisms. The other line of explanation is the assumption that the optical isomers now found in living things were included by chance by the first living organism and have since been handed down from generation to generation. Life arose not as a single case but probably repetitively at the time of its origin. Chance incorporation of optical isomers would establish some forms with L-amino acid and D-sugar composition and others with D-amino acids and L-sugars. But there is a distinct advantage in having one type of food chain for all organisms, and this advantage would be realized if one type "won out" over the other, which is the way Wald proposes that the present situation came about; in essence it was "natural selection on the molecular level."

The Origin of Petroleum

It was inevitable that a bitter controversy should arise over the question of the origin of petroleum. As long as the theory prevailed that only living things could synthesize organic compounds, it was natural that a theory of a biogenic origin of petroleum would be formulated. In time, an impressive amount of evidence accumulated. It became generally accepted that organic compounds, especially the fats and oils of billions of generations of organisms, contributed to the formation of vast amounts of petroleum. The evidence is primarily geological and geochemical. Geologists for the most part have taken a strong stand for the biogenic origin of petroleum. However, proof for the abiogenic synthesis of organic compounds in prebiological times is now almost overwhelming. There is as little doubt now that hydrocarbons can form abiogenically as there is that products of organisms can be converted to hydrocarbons. At the least, the abiogenic origin of petroleum must be given a place along with the biogenic theory. Sylvester-Bradley and King[14] recently reviewed briefly the evidence for abiogenic hydrocarbons. Cautiously they state: "We are not suggesting that the evidence we have quoted in this article is conclusive, but we do believe that it is sufficiently suggestive to admit the abiogenic theory to the status of a working hypothsis." The position for the "duplex origin of petroleum" is briefly stated by Robinson.[15] The most ardent support for the abiogenic view comes from Soviet geologists. Kropotkin[16] admits no other but the abiogenic origin of petroleum.

The Energy Factor

Potential reactants must be activated by some form of energy so that they will enter into a mutual reaction spontaneously. The primitive atmosphere came under the influence of a variety of energies. The intensity of solar and cosmic radiation has probably changed little in the history of the earth. Electric discharges might have been greater in the past. The rate of decay of radioactive elements is extremely precise, so the past contribution from this source can be calculated accurately from present values in any locality. Geologic methods permit calculations on the extent of volcanic activity for the past billion years, but there are variables which make conclusions uncertain.

Electric discharges produce parts of the electromagnetic spectrum; these electric discharges generate heat and strong electric fields in which ionization of gases can take place. The energized particles may in turn emit energy in a characteristic wavelength which can serve as the activating source for other atoms and molecules. This complexity may be the basis for the reported greater efficacy of electric sparking over other forms of energy in the experiments on production of organic compounds under presumed primitive conditions.

The contribution of radioactive decay and cosmic rays to the energy pool was probably not large. Although radioactivity was much greater (2–3.5 times) in the past, the position of radioelements in the lithosphere, many of them at great depths, made radioactivity less effective than other sources for energizing reactions in the atmosphere.

Thermal energy sources were sporadic and not always located in the same place. The effectiveness of this type of intermittent bursts of energy has not been studied sufficiently. While high temperatures may favor interaction among the gases, such temperatures generally hasten the decomposition of the products. But intermittency may be a desirable critical factor in the case of thermal energy. The temporarily high temperature may favor the rapid production of intermediates. With a drop in temperature the decomposition of the intermediates decreases, while the production from them of higher molecular weight substances is favored.

Ultrasonic vibrations have also been suggested as an energy source in the activation of reactants.[17] Exposure of a mixture of nitrogen and hydrogen in distilled water to ultrasonic vibrations yielded measurable amounts of ammonia. Distilled water, carbon monoxide, hydrogen, and nitrogen, under the same conditions gave measurable amounts of formaldehyde. These findings cannot be properly evaluated because the quantity of ultrasonic vibrations at the time in question is an unknown factor.

The most recent addition to this array of energies is hypersonics. Hochstim[18] has calculated the effect of the entrance of meteorites in the atmosphere (Fig. 7-1) and has come up with some surprising and impressive figures. A meteorite with a radius of 500 meters and a velocity of 11 km/sec will have 400,000 tons of gas in its stagnation region compressed to 1500 atmospheres pressure and a temperature of $16,300°K$! Its kinetic energy will be equivalent to 40,000 megatons of

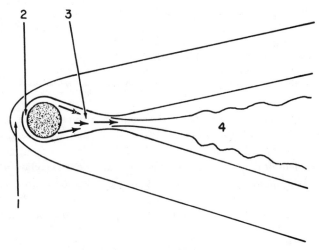

Fig. 7-1. Hypersonic Flow Around Meteorite. (1) Stagnation region. (2) Boundary layer. (3) Ablating (evaporating) species. (4) Inner wake. From Hochstim, A. R., *Proc. Natl. Acad. Sci.* **50**, 200 (1963).

TNT. The chemical reactivity engendered by this is equally impressive and will be mentioned below.

Reaction Mechanisms

Reaction mechanisms are diverse and depend on the nature of the energy involved. Moderate elevations of temperature will favor reactivity between compounds by supplying the initial energy of activation for spontaneous reactions or the continuous energy for endergonic reactions. Reaction between various molecular species may be brought about by mild energy forms. Bahadur's scheme[19] for the synthesis of all the amino acids from formaldehyde, ammonia, and suitable catalysts requires only light and results in the formation of monoamino and monocarboxylic acids. Bahadur's scheme in the synthesis of glycine is modified as follows:

Glycine

$$O + 2CH_2O \rightleftharpoons HOCH_2COOH$$
$$HOCH_2COOH \rightleftharpoons CHOCOOH + 2H$$
$$CHOCOOH + 2NH_3 \rightleftharpoons NHCHCOONH_4$$
$$NHCHCOONH_4 + 2H \rightleftharpoons NH_2CH_2COONH_4$$
$$NH_2CH_2COONH_4 + H_2O \rightleftharpoons NH_2CH_2COOH + NH_3$$

Glycine

The synthesis of an additional seventeen amino acids is detailed in a similar vein by Bahadur. The suggested reaction routes are, for the most part, as follows: condensation, hydration, dehydration, oxidation, reduction, and decarboxylation.

In the spark-type experiments hydrogen cyanide is an early product. It may have several origins. Hydrogen cyanide can form directly from the interaction between methane and ammonia:

$$CH_4 + NH_3 \rightarrow HCN + 3H_2$$

Other hydrocarbons, as they form, can also give rise to hydrogen cyanide on reacting with ammonia, for example:

$$C_2H_2 + 2NH_3 \rightarrow 2HCN + 3H_2$$

Carbon monoxide is still another possible source for hydrogen cyanide:

$$CO + NH_3 \rightarrow HCN + H_2O$$

A possible origin of the carbon monoxide may be methane:

$$CH_4 + H_2O \rightarrow CO + 3H_2$$

In the spark, methane will form carbon–carbon bonds yielding two-carbon compounds, for example, C_2H_2, C_2H_4, C_2H_6. In the presence of hydrogen cyanide, the hydrocarbons yield nitriles:

$$C_2H_4 + HCN \rightarrow CH_3CH_2CN$$

Propionitrile

or $\quad C_2H_2 + 2HCN \rightarrow NCCH_2CH_2CN$

Succinodinitrile

The corresponding acids are obtained when the nitriles are hydrolyzed in the aqueous phase:

$$CH_3CH_2CN + 2H_2O \rightarrow CH_3CH_2COOH + NH_3$$
Propionic acid

$$NCCH_2CH_2CN + 4H_2O \rightarrow HOOCCH_2CH_2COOH + 2NH_3$$
Succinic acid

With hydrogen cyanide, aldehydes form the corresponding hydroxynitriles, which on hydrolysis will yield the hydroxy acids.

$$H_2CO + HCN \rightleftharpoons CH_2OHCN \xrightarrow{2H_2O} CH_2OHCOOH + NH_3$$
Formaldehyde   Glycolic acid

$$CH_3CHO + HCN \rightleftharpoons CH_3CHOHCN \xrightarrow{2H_2O}$$
Acetaldehyde

$$CH_3CHOHCOOH + NH_3$$
Lactic Acid

$$CH_3CH_2CHO + HCN \rightleftharpoons CH_3CH_2CHOHCN \xrightarrow{2H_2O}$$
Propionaldehyde

$$CH_3CH_2CHOHCOOH + NH_3$$
α-Hydroxybutyric acid

With ammonia, the hydroxynitriles can form the corresponding aminonitriles from which the amino acids may be obtained by hydrolysis:

$$CH_2OHCN \xrightarrow{NH_3} CH_2NH_2CN + H_2O$$
$$\downarrow 2H_2O$$
$$CH_2NH_2COOH + NH_3$$
Glycine

$$CH_3CHOHCN \xrightarrow{NH_3} CH_3CHNH_2CN + H_2O$$
$$\downarrow 2H_2O$$
$$CH_3CHNH_2COOH + NH_3$$
Alanine

$$CH_3CH_2CHOHCN \xrightarrow{NH_3} CH_3CH_2CHNH_2CN + H_2O$$

$$\downarrow 2H_2O$$

$$CH_3CH_2CHNH_2COOH + NH_3$$

α-Aminobutyric acid

The mechanism of formation of the β-amino acid β-alanine probably follows a different course. Ammonia makes a nucleophilic attack on the β carbon of acrylonitrile or acrylamide, and the resulting compound undergoes hydrolysis to β-alanine:

$$CH_2CHCN \xrightarrow{NH_3} CH_2NH_2CH_2CN \xrightarrow{2H_2O}$$

Acrylonitrile $\qquad$ β-Aminopropionitrile

$$CH_2NH_2CH_2COO + NH_3$$

β-Alanine

$$CH_2CHCONH_2 \xrightarrow{NH_3} CH_2CH\cdots\overset{\overset{\displaystyle NH_2}{|}}{C}\cdots O \xrightarrow{H_2O}$$

Acrylamide $\qquad$ β-Aminopropionamide

$$CH_2NH_2CH_2COO^- + NH_3$$

β-Alanine

Ionizing radiation, very high temperature, and electric sparking create high energy species. Under the impact of sufficient energy, compounds become dissociated and give rise to free radicals, neutral species, and ions. The results of the interaction among these can be very complex and practically unpredictable. A good example is the report of Hochstim[18] on "hypersonic chemosynthesis." The high temperature and pressure created by the entry of the meteorite, mentioned above, into the atmosphere, will convert the atoms of all compounds present into excited species. The same kinds of ions and free radicals will form, whether the atmosphere contained CO, CO_2, CH_4 (or other hydrocarbon source), NH_3, NO_2,

NO (or other nitrogen source), H_2S, SO_2 (or other sulfur source), etc. The energetic species would be C, C^+, O, O^+, e^-, N, N^+, H, H^+, OH, NO, NO^+, S, etc. Behind the meteorite, lower temperatures are encountered, and combinations can take place: N_2, O_2, C_2, H_2, C_3, O_3, C_4, N_2^+, H_2^+, O_2^+, CO, CO_2, CH, CH_2, CH_4, CH^+, CN, CN^+, C_2N_2, NH, NH_2, NO, N_2O, NO_2, NH_3, OH, NO^+, H_2O, HS, H_2S, SO, SO_2, etc. Evaporation from the meteorite would yield Fe, Fe^+, Ni, Ni^+, P, PO, FeO, CuO, FeN, FeC, etc. Impact with water would mix water vapor with the reactive species and would result in formation of simple and complex organic compounds. In preliminary experiments a high velocity bullet was fired through a mixture of CH_4, NH_3, and H_2 into water. The water was found to contain organic compounds.

Kliss and Matthews[20] proposed an interesting hypothesis in 1962 in which they suggest that activated hydrogen cyanide dimerizes into a biradical intermediate, aminocyanocarbene. Polymerization of this intermediate and subsequent modification of various types of polymers could yield proteins, purines, pyrimidines, and sugars. The authors suggest the following mechanisms. The biradical forms as follows:

$$2\text{HCN} \rightarrow \text{H}_2\text{N}-\dot{\text{C}}-\text{C}\equiv\text{N} \rightleftharpoons \text{H}_2\text{N}-\dot{\text{C}}=\text{C}=\dot{\text{N}}$$

1,1-Biradical form 1,3-Biradical form
of aminocyanocarbene of aminocyanocarbene

Formation of a precursor to polyglycine occurs by head-to-tail polymerization of the 1,3 biradical, followed by tautomerization and, in turn, followed by hydrogenation:

$$=\text{N}(\overset{\overset{\textstyle \text{NH}_2}{|}}{\text{C}}=\text{C}=\text{N})_n\overset{\overset{\textstyle \text{NH}_2}{|}}{\text{C}}=\text{C}= \xrightarrow{\text{tautomerization}}$$

$$-\text{HN}(\overset{\overset{\textstyle \text{NH}}{\|}}{\text{C}}\text{C}\text{NH})_n\overset{\overset{\textstyle \text{NH}}{\|}}{\text{C}}\text{C}- \xrightarrow{\text{hydrogenation}} -\text{HN}(\overset{\overset{\textstyle \text{NH}}{\|}}{\text{C}}\text{CH}_2\text{NH})_n\overset{\overset{\textstyle \text{NH}}{\|}}{\text{C}}\text{CH}_2-$$

Polyglycine precursor

The precursor polymer molecules would tend to form both right-handed and left-handed α-helices. One of the hydrogens of each methylene group would be directed toward the center and the other toward the outside. This exposed hydrogen would be susceptible to attack by excited species. Appropriate substitution at these points would introduce the various side chains of amino acids and, at the same time, create centers of optical asymmetry. The configuration of all the asymmetric units in a particular coil will be either L or D, depending solely on the direction in which that coil turns. Substitution of imino groups by oxygen radicals would establish the peptide backbone of proteins. Reaction mechanisms are also described which yield purines, pyrimidines, and sugars from activated dimers and monomers.

As can be seen, the reaction mechanisms range all the way from those usually found in the metabolism of present organisms to highly energetic reactions inimical to life. The latter type are more attractive as an explanation of prebiological synthesis. They are simpler and usually less variable. Complexity and variability of biosynthetic pathways are probably the result of hundreds of millions of years of innovation by biological systems.

References

1. Blum, H. F., in Rudnick, D., ed., "Rhythmic and Synthetic Growth Processes," Princeton University Press, Princeton, N. J., 1957.
2. _____, *Am. Scientist* **49,** 474 (1961).
3. _____, "Time's Arrow and Evolution," 2nd ed. revised, Harper & Row Publishers, New York, 1962.
4. Horowitz, N. H., in Oparin, A. I., ed., "The Origin of Life on the Earth" (I. U. B. Sympos. Series Vol. 1), Pergamon Press, New York, 1959, p. 106.
5. Urey, H. C., "The Planets," Yale University Press, New Haven, Conn., 1952, pp. 152–3.

6. Bernal, J. D., in Oparin, A. I., ed., "The Origin of Life on the Earth" (I. U. B. Sympos, Series, Vol. 1), Pergamon Press, New York, 1959, p. 38.

7. Fox, S. W., *Science* **132,** 200 (1960).

8. Wald, G., *Annals N. Y. Acad. Sci.* **69,** 352 (1957).

9. Oparin, A. I., "Origin of Life," Academic Press, New York, 1957 pp. 189–96.

10. Natta, G., Pino, P., Mazzanti, G., and Longi, P., *Gazz. chim. ital.* **88,** 219 (1958).

11. Gabriel, M., *Am. Naturalist* **94,** 257 (1960).

12. Winstein, S., and Lucas, H. J., *J. Am. Chem. Soc.* **61,** 1576 (1939).

13. Harada, K., *Nature* **200,** 1201 (1963).

14. Sylvester-Bradley, P. C., and King, R. J., *Nature* **198,** 728 (1963).

15. Robinson, R., *Nature* **199,** 113 (1963).

16. Kropotkin, P. N., in Oparin, A. I., ed., "The Origin of Life on Earth" (I. U. B. Sympos. Series Vol. 1) Pergamon Press, New York, 1959, p. 84.

17. Elpiner, E., and Sokolskaya, A. V., in Oparin, A. I., ed., "The Origin of Life on the Earth" (I. U. B. Sympos. Series, Vol. 1), Pergamon Press, New York, 1959, p. 172.

18. Hochstim, A. R., *Proc. Natl. Acad. Sci. U. S.* **50,** 200 (1963).

19. Bahadur, K., in Oparin, A. I., ed., "The Origin of Life on the Earth" (I. U. B. Sympos. Series, Vol. 1), Pergamon Press, New York, 1959, p. 140.

20. Kliss, R. M., and Matthews, C. N., *Proc. Natl. Acad. Sci. U. S.* **48,** 1300 (1962).

chapter eight

Summing Up

With the publication of substantial theories by Haldane in 1928 and by Oparin in both 1924 and 1936, the age-old problem of the origin of life entered a new era. Moreover, Oparin's work in 1936 was detailed enough to be put to experimental test. However, it was not until 1953, that the now classical experiments of Miller ushered in the present era of prolific and productive experimentation. Thus, in 1953, Miller established unequivocally that organic compounds can be synthesized from a simple gas mixture which was like the composition of the primitive atmosphere proposed by Oparin. In the mixture used by Miller, the gases were methane, ammonia, water vapor, and hydrogen; the energy source utilized for the synthesis was electric sparking. In the ensuing 10 yrs, however, a variety of gas mixtures has been tried, and diverse energy sources from ultrasonics to gamma rays have been employed in conjunction with those gas mixtures. In addition to gases, simple compounds in solution (such as formaldehyde and glycol, along with nitrates or other nitrogen sources) have been used with success in the synthesis of organic compounds. The number and kinds of organic compounds that form under these presumed primitive earth conditions are surprising. Amino acids appear almost invariably; moreover, they are generally of the α-amino variety associated with living things. Other products reported as having been synthesized under primitive earth conditions include a variety of organic acids, aldehydes, ketones, alcohols, amides, amines, purines, pyrimidines, nucleosides, nucleotides, and some nucleotide polymers, porphyrins, glycosidic polymers, and amino acid polymers (proteinoids).

It was not entirely unexpected that controversies should arise. Theories on the origin of life have many facets, all of them in dispute in some measure, as for instance, the time and manner of formation of the earth and its atmosphere, the composition of the primitive atmosphere, the kinds of organic compounds that would form from such an atmosphere, the mechanism of further increase in complexity of organic compounds, the nature and magnitude of the energy required to drive the chemical reactions, and the mechanism of formation of the first living things.

No one set of conditions for the primitive earth and its atmosphere has been universally accepted. Experimenters proceed on assumptions that they consider most likely. These assumptions vary all the way from primitive earth conditions similar to the present, to conditions that picture the primitive earth as a hot body with a seething turbulent atmosphere of gases that would be noxious to any present-day living thing. However, the proposed starting conditions are merely a point of departure for specific ideas on organic chemical synthesis. The surprising realization that is emerging is that organic compounds of much the same variety, if not abundance, can be expected not from one, but from quite a number of different starting mixtures under the influence of many different energy types.

One limitation for organic chemical synthesis from simple gases seems to be that reducing conditions must prevail. However, given these reducing conditions, the carbon source need not be in reduced state (e.g. methane), but could be even in its most oxidized state (carbon dioxide). The same holds true also for the sources of nitrogen, phosphorus, and sulfur. Moreover, even the general requirement of reducing conditions is removed if a highly energetic source is employed to activate the reactions. For example, the high heat caused by the entry of a large meteorite into an atmosphere creates free radicals, neutral species, and ions from any and all compounds in its path. The composition of the ambient atmosphere is immaterial. Thus, when the meteorite strikes water, an abundance of organic compounds will form.

Backed by all the recent experimental evidence, it is now safe to take for granted the existence of a great variety of organic compounds in prebiological times from which to start reconstructing the origin of the first living things. However, we can be too sanguine in this assumption, and take too much for granted. We might be tempted to assume that before organisms came there already were complex proteins, coded nucleic acids, special compounds (such as cytochromes and chlorophyll), and metabolic pathways like the ones found in present organisms. On the contrary, a good deal of room must be left for continuing organic chemical evolution in organisms. We must not lose sight of the fact that the problem is not to produce a replica of a present-day "primitive" microorganism. Nothing is gained thereby in terms of the *origin* of life. Often, surmises on the possible structure and metabolism of the first living things are claimed to be the result of *extrapolation* backward from what is known about present primitive organisms, when actually a relatively unchanged modern mechanism has merely been *transferred* backward some two billion years.

Two Approaches

The approach to an understanding of how living things came into being has taken two main lines. According to one theory, the first living thing was a gene. But since the gene, like a virus, cannot function in the absence of an already well-coordinated metabolic system, this theory amounts to postulating the all-at-once origin of cytoplasm and nuclear material.

The other line of approach assumes the preliminary separation of minute macromolecular systems from the general environment. These systems develop further with the incorporation of substances from the environment, gradually increasing the complexity of internal organization and metabolic capacities to the level of living things. The coacervates of Oparin and the microspheres of Fox are examples of the second line of approach. At the present, there is more emphasis placed on experimentation concerning the synthesis of various biochemicals under presumed primitive earth conditions than on the origin of first living things from inanimate multimolecular systems. However, a shift in the latter direction is bound to occur sooner or later.

The subject of the origin of life is beginning to accumulate a vocabulary of its own. Pirie suggested that the origin of the first living thing, including the chemical history that preceded it, be termed biopoesis and that the word eobiont be used to designate this first "organism." These terms are well coined and have come into use. To the horror of some biologists the term natural selection is employed freely to indicate the process by which the prevalence of one type of molecule over another possible type might have taken place or the process by which a nonliving macromolecular system might grow increasingly complex on its way to becoming an eobiont. Macromolecular systems that could be candidates for future eobionts are called prebiological systems. Bernal uses "subvital" in the same sense.

Conclusion

An attempt to summarize the salient features of the origin of life is presented in Fig. 8-1. In this figure, the word eobiogenesis appears. Eobiogenesis is derived from Pirie's eobiont and is intended to herald the first successful emergence of eobionts from well-developed subvital structures. The three

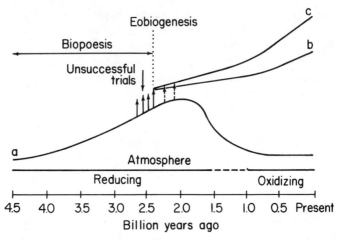

Fig. 8-1. Main Milestones in the Theory of the Origin of Life. See text for explanation.

arrows preceding eobiogenesis indicate a period of rise and dissolution of less developed subvital structures, that is, a period of "trial and error." The line *a* follows the progress of abiogenic organic chemical evolution. The rise in line *a* should be interpreted as an increase in quantity and complexity of organic compounds in time. The sharp drop in line *a* is to be expected after living things became well established and began to consume rapidly the ready-made organic compounds. The two dotted arrows from line *a* near its apex indicate possible repetitions of eobiogenesis. It is not entirely warranted to assume that only one eobiont formed at only one point in the past. I think the assumption is more logical that when conditions favored eobiogenesis, this event occurred in many places for a continuing period of time.

Line *c* indicates the rise of increasingly more complex organisms, in other words, biological evolution. The increase in its slope is meant to coincide with the change from anaerobic to aerobic metabolism. This change permitted a more efficient utilization of energy, and increased the rate of evolution. Line *b* indicates the period of biogenic synthesis of organic compounds, which has supplanted abiogenic synthesis. The figure attempts also to show roughly the transition of the atmosphere from a reducing character to an oxidizing one. This transition of the atmospheric character occurred more or less gradually as the primitive atmosphere was used up in the process of synthesis of organic compounds and as autotrophic organisms, liberating oxygen, evolved from the original heterotrophs.

chapter nine

Speculations

Not so long ago the answers to the problem of the first origin of life were speculative and entirely based on imagination; one might say they were wholly in the realm of science fiction. Now that a scientifically acceptable explanation is emerging for the origin of life on earth, many scientists feel that the time has come to rescue the concept of life in the universe from its hitherto fictional status. Some of the thinking along these lines will be presented in the next section. The material basis and the conditions necessary for the coming into being of living things have never ceased to exist since life was first established. However, on many grounds, the following views are maintained: that life originated only once in the past; that neobiogenesis (the origin of life anew) did not and cannot occur; and that, therefore, all organisms past and present are descendants of the first organisms. In the last section, the evidence against neobiogenesis is reexamined in the light of the recent work on the origin of life and is found not to be as convincing as was supposed.

EXTRATERRESTRIAL LIFE

An ancient myth tells of the wood chopper who did not heed the Sabbath but worked as on ordinary days. His punishment was severe—he was exiled to the moon. There, his shadowy form darkly outlined against the luminous background, he was to warn forever other would-be offenders of the grim fate awaiting them. This mythical "man on the moon," however, was an immigrant extraterrestrial being, not a native moon dweller.

Aside from ubiquitous myths, life in the universe was contemplated early by Anaxagoras, who in his panspermic ideas saw life as "ethereal germs" dispersed throughout the world. With Copernicus' revolutionary pronouncement of a heliocentric system, as opposed to the widely accepted Ptolemean geocentric view, thoughts turned again to the possibility of life on other planets. This was first expressed in the sixteenth century by Giordano Bruno who wrote: "There are innumerable suns and innumerable earths, which revolve around our sun ...These worlds are inhabited by living creatures." Too advanced for the times, this brilliant deduction was condemned as heresy and its author burned at the stake.

By the end of the seventeenth century, however, the heliocentric idea was firmly established, and Bernard de Fontenelle could safely assume "many worlds" whose inhabitants had character traits that matched the observed behavior of their home planets (Mercurians are vivacious, Saturnians dull, etc.,).

Fiction writers, too, have been frequently inspired by the thought of life in space; among many others, one need only mention Cyrano de Bergerac who directed his famous nose toward the moon ("Histoire Comique des États de la Lune") and, of course, the dean of all science-fiction writers Jules Verne ("De la Terre à la Lune"). Thus, "science fiction" is not a recent side line of advanced technology, but a natural outgrowth of the interest and burning curiosity engendered by possible extraterrestrial companions in the adventure of life.

Real progress in the investigation of possible life in the universe had to come once again first from astronomy and then from other allied fields of science. Harlow Shapley has assembled a strong, though still largely circumstantial body of evidence, for the existence of extraterrestrial life. Starting from the premise that life can begin chemically and struggle successfully to persist under favorable conditions, he deduces that it must occur in nearly all star systems that carry earth-like planets.

Since our solar system was the closest at hand, it was the first to be surveyed by all presently available means of exploration; however, only two planets have passed as likely supporters of some instance of life—besides, of course, earth. Mars with its thin, cold air, containing little oxygen and possibly some liquid water in "summer," bars higher forms of life but would not be too inimical to lichenlike organisms. In fact, so-called simulation experiments proved that even certain terrestrial microorganisms could survive the rigorous Martian conditions. The spectrometric analysis of the dark areas on Mars points to their organic origin and thus supports the contention that life could exist there. Jupiter is another planet recently reconsidered as suitable for living organisms, since its thick atmosphere might act as a blanket to reduce the loss of heat from its surface. The thickness of the atmosphere is important, as less heat reaches Jupiter in the first place because of its greater distance from the sun.

Next, our Milky Way has been eyed for earthlike planets. Many stars in our galaxy should be accompanied by planets, though proof for this supposition still awaits the further refinement of astronomic instruments. The same is considered to be true for the myriad of external galaxies. Indeed, there may be a total star population of over 10^{20}, and at least ten billion earthlike planets among these stars, after the following restrictive conditions are taken into account.

(1) The star must be fairly stable. The evolution of life, though probably running a similar course anywhere in the universe, is highly random. However, the evolution of stars is more predictable. Luminosity increases as the fourth power of the star's mass; therefore, the most luminous stars are also

the most massive and the hottest ones. If plotted as a graph, the hottest stars follow a "main-sequence" classified in descending order as spectral types O, B, A, F, G, K, and M. Further relative temperature differences are indicated by the added designation of "early" or "late." A star that is very high in the sequence burns up too quickly for the biological evolutionary time scale; a star that has already left the main-sequence releases so much energy that it would destroy living organisms. Of all the spectral classes late F-, G-, and early K-type stars offer the best possibility for the establishment of life. Our sun is an early G-type star, and other stars like it will fulfill the conditions of a stable source of radiant heat.

(2) The planetary orbit must be approximately circular. Because stars evolved out of dust clouds, many stars are double, triple, or in clusters, and therefore hostile to life-bearing planets. Such planets would have to travel in a thermally adequate and stable orbit that is fairly circular. Single stars are best suited for this condition. (3) The presence of liquid water and (4) "nonpoisonous" surroundings (air, oceans, and soil) need no further discussion.

Thus, with 10 billion likely planets, there must be quite an incidence of life throughout the universe. To all appearances, however, there is not another lifebearing solar system in our immediate corner of the Milky Way. The nearest possibility, Tau Ceti, which is also an early G star like our sun, is over ten light-years away. This is a short distance in astronomical terms, but it seems unlikely that we could bridge this "astronomic" distance in our life time. Our earth started some 4.5 billion years ago, and the beginning of life has been put at 2.5 billion years; yet, our technology is still in its infancy. Only during the last decade have we come to the point where we can gingerly "stick a toe" into the vast unknown ocean of space.

Still, some astronomers thought that communication attempts with Tau Ceti should be instituted by monitoring possible radio signals from outer space. The wavelength of 21.1 cm (hydrogen emission) was chosen as most propitious because atmospheric as well as galactic noises are negligible in that range and because the importance of this wavelength might have also occurred to extraterrestrial astronomers. F. Drake[1] of the National Radio Astronomy Observatory at Green Bank, W. Virginia, actually started a project in 1960, which used an 85 ft radiotelescope for intercepting signals and which had already devised a code based on cardinal numbers repeated in regular intervals. This system, though at the conversational level of "babytalk," was to be only a beginning. Since then, however, the project has been abandoned.

How valid are the estimates of the extent to which life is distributed throughout the universe? We do not know. At one extreme is the deterministic approach, which assumes that life very likely originates on any favorable earthlike planet.[2-6] The other extreme is the opportunistic approach, which cautiously considers that the origin of life is the result of such an improbable concatenation of events and circumstances that even under favorable conditions the distribution of life in the universe must be considered to be sparse, if not unique.[7,8] Although Shapley believes that life must have originated on most of the 10^{10} earthlike planets extant, he is more conservative about accepting the possibility that humanlike beings and intelligence are as abundant.

The progress of inorganic compounds to organic compounds, organic compounds to macromolecules, macromolecules to macromolecular swarms and systems, and eventually, these systems to living systems is explained by assuming the existence at any stage of the materials and principles for the development of the next stage. Given the same starting conditions (any time and any place), the same sequence of stages is to be expected. Nevertheless, many scientists, taking the deterministic view with regard to the origin of life, proclaim the possibility that life is practically omnipresent but still do not expect manlike beings and intelligence to be as abundant as the number of favorable earthlike planets might indicate.

On the other hand, the view can be taken that the origin of life represents an extremely rare event even under favorable conditions and that the evolution of manlike organisms from an original living thing is even rarer. This view, the opportunistic view, looks upon the succession of stages, particularly as it applies to biological evolution, as the result of chance happenings from among which there will be survivals only through natural selection. If during the history of the earth different conditions had prevailed at certain critical periods in evolution, the whole array of present day organisms might be different also. The possibility that any other planet repeated the exact history of the earth, short of which manlike beings could not evolve, is considered negligible, and many who hold the opportunistic view regard the human being as unique in the universe.

A point can be made for merging the two views into one. The simpler chemical evolution affords few opportunities for variation; the same products result from a variety of conditions (Chapter 8, pages 87, 88). However, the outcome of the reactions among more complex chemicals is more dependent on environmental conditions and yields a variety of products, each determined by its specific conditions. Biological evolution, where the complexity is even greater, is also dependent on environmental conditions. Each of a variety of descendants of a common ancestor harks back to a specific set of conditions prevailing at the time of its origin and not to accidents or errors.

NEOBIOGENESIS

By raising the question of whether or not neobiogenesis is possible, I do not intend to resurrect the spontaneous generation controversy. Although both terms imply that life can originate from inanimate matter, the comparison ends there. The term spontaneous generation has been applied to the all-at-once origin out of inanimate substances of all manner of organisms from microbes to man. Often some "life-force" is added to the recipe. It is best, therefore, neither to take this term out of its historical context nor to apply it to any other specific concept.

Neobiogenesis is akin to eobiogenesis. As has been pointed out, life originated only after organic compounds of a high degree of complexity were available. Then, macromolecules could separate out of the environment in discrete structures in conjunction with various compounds, eventually to evolve into living systems. The exact manner in which this occurred is immaterial for this argument. It could have been through coacervation, or it could have been through a nucleic acid or nucleoprotein that "commandeered" an appropriate environment in which to function. When enough facts have accumulated to permit experimentation at this level, it is almost certain that any number of variations will be possible, resulting in the formation of as many different living metabolic systems. The word eobiogenesis designates the first instance of life. The word neobiogenesis is employed here to describe the repeated origination of life in nature ever since life began. Is neobiogenesis possible?

The answer is almost always an unhesitating, impatient, and even angry NO! This is a reflection of the attitude "Is this not the same old tired claim of spontaneous generation, the thoroughly discredited medieval superstition?" "How often in the past has science painstakingly examined such claims only to find them based on faulty experiments, misunderstandings, or even charlatanism?'' Yet, with the rapid accumulation of facts including successful experiments bearing on the preliminary aspects of the problem of the origin of life, many scientists today seriously consider the possibility of the experimental synthesis of a living system to be only a matter of time; nevertheless, the same persons will maintain that nature is unable to initiate life anew.

This is strange indeed! It is reminiscent of the days when chemists already were synthesizing organic compounds of all kinds while it was still being maintained that this could not take place in nature unaided by living things. However, it is now evident that nature anticipated man by some four billion years in the synthesis of organic compounds. Now we find that it is being claimed that nature is unable to initiate life anew, whereas man will be successful. The arguments to support this stand are for the most part the old ones and are no longer valid in the light of our present understanding of the origin of life.[9] Newer and more sophisticated objections are no more valid than the old ones. Let us examine the objections presently being put forth.

(1) There is first of all the view that spontaneous generation was disproved once and for all by Pasteur a century ago and that this holds for neobiogenesis also. (2) The origin of life from inorganic beginnings took over two billion years to occur, and there has not been that much time available since that occurrence for it to have happened again. (3) The conditions under which life originated were unique and will never occur again. On these grounds, the re-origin of life is impossible. (4) A newly arising form cannot survive against the competition from already well-established forms. (5) The biochemical evidence points to a common ancestry for all living things. This indicates that life did occur only once, and all subsequent forms are descendants of it. (6) If neobiogenesis were possible, it should have been detected by now, considering the

tens of thousands of trained observers past and present, engaged in microbiological and allied fields.

1. The Pasteur Experiments

As previously mentioned, neobiogenesis is not the same as spontaneous generation. However, contrary to popular belief, not even the concept of spontaneous generation has ever been disproved experimentally. Specific claims of the creation of a particular kind of living thing by a given procedure have been disproved individually but never the concept itself. It is instructive to examine some of Pasteur's experiments in the spontaneous generation controversy to see what valid conclusions may be drawn from them.

Pasteur's experiments were simple and ingenious.[10] He tested infusions similar to the ones Pouchet (Chapter 2) had employed in his positive claims of successful spontaneous generation, and at the same time showed that it was indeed the surrounding air which carried the contaminating germs to a greater or lesser degree. After vigorously boiling the mixtures in round glass flasks with long drawn-out necks (Fig. 9-1), he heat-sealed the tips and allowed the contents to cool. The flasks that he broke open in the quiet air of a cellar were only rarely contaminated in contrast to the ones that he

Fig. 9-1. Pasteur Flask with Drawn-out Straight Neck.

opened in turbulent air. With brilliant insight, he even carried some of his sterile flasks up to a high Alpine glacier and
found most of them to be germ-free several days after having
broken them open. Pouchet interpreted Pasteur's findings to
support his own claim of spontaneous generation; the broth
was ripe for microbes to be generated, and all that was necessary was for the essential components of air to be admitted
into the flask to energize the process.

Pasteur got around this argument with the more elaborate
apparatus shown in Fig. 9-2. In the apparatus, a platinum

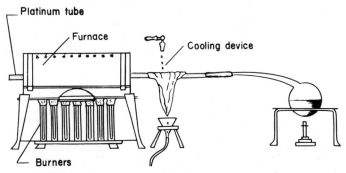

Fig. 9-2. Apparatus for Sterilizing Air. Cooling device cools the hot air before
entry into the flask.

tube runs through a small furnace heated by burners, and its
other end connects with the neck of the flask. After the contents of the flask are boiled so that steam issues from the end
of the platinum tube, the tube is brought to red heat and the
flask is allowed to cool. As it cools, air is sucked back first
through the red-hot tube, then through the portion which is
kept cool with running water, and finally into the flask. Thus,
air is readmitted but only after the contaminating microbes
have been destroyed. The failure of life to appear in the flasks
under these conditions was attributed by Pouchet to the

destruction of essential components of air by the excessive heat. The man could be exasperating! But Pasteur got around this too, with a new type of flask (Fig. 9-3a), the design of which was suggested to him by his friend Balard, the discoverer of bromine. The new flask was like the first,

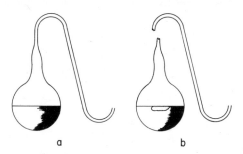

a   b

Fig. 9-3. Flasks with S-shaped Necks. (a) Unbroken neck; contents of flask uncontaminated. (b) Flask with broken neck; contents of flask contaminated.

but with a longer neck drawn out into an S-shape. As the steam from the boiling mixture passed through the neck of the flask, some of it condensed and collected as water in the lower curve. When the flask cooled, the air was sucked back through the water and was washed clean of dust and microbes. Although some flasks showed contamination, the majority remained clear until the neck was broken (Fig. 9-3b).

This was the nature of the experiments that won for Pasteur the award of the French Academy of Science and that convinced most of his contemporaries and posterity that the possibility of spontaneous generation had been thereby disproved once and for all. This is obviously not so. He simply proved that certain mixtures (and they were of relatively few kinds) when treated in a certain way would not give rise to living forms. The results of these experiments do not disprove that another type of mixture treated in some other way will give rise to life.

The difficulty lies in the nature of negative proof. The negative result of an experiment indicates the failure of that experiment but does not necessarily preclude the possibility of the success of subsequent trials or of variations of the original experiment. Only when all possible combinations of materials and techniques have proved futile can a negative answer be valid. But this is impossible in the case of the concept of spontaneous generation. The number of combinations of possible starting materials and treatments is truly infinite. Even if we knew what materials to use, boiling is out of the question since it would denature some of the starting materials. By no scientific standard can it rightfully be said that Pasteur had put the *concept* of spontaneous generation to the test.

2. The Time Factor

It is estimated that the origin of life from inorganic beginnings took about 2–2.5 billion years. Most of this time was consumed by the preliminary synthesis, first of organic compounds and then of macromolecular systems that were the immediate precursors of the first living things. All of these events leading to and including the origin of life are covered by the word biopoesis. Biopoesis can be divided arbitrarily into two phases. The first covers the period of physical and chemical processes in the abiotic synthesis of macromolecular systems. The second, eobiogenesis, includes the transformation of macromolecular systems into the first living things (Fig. 8-1).

Neobiogenesis eliminates the first phase. Ever since life first began, the necessary variety of organic compounds and macromolecular systems on which the re-origin of life would depend have always been present. Indeed, living things have added to the variety and complexity of such systems. Neobiogenesis today can start from systems closer to the living state than was the case at the first origin of life. It is possible that the transformation of subvital systems into living things under the proper conditions may be a matter only of minutes instead of eons.

Inanimate organic systems of a higher degree of complexity and reactivity than the primitive coacervates, etc., constantly form today from the activities of living things. An enucleated ameba can continue to synthesize proteins and carry on other activities for many days. This is true for enucleated cells of some other types and may be generally true. Single cells extrude globules of cellular material into the environment and often fragment completely when handled roughly during micromanipulation. As the globules and fragments first appear, there is a momentary oozing into the environmental fluid as though a complete diffusion were about to take place, and this does often occur. But often also, the globule or fragment suddenly becomes stabilized. It is as though a membrane whips around the outside and prevents further disintegration.

The composition of such isolated units must vary even when derived from the same cell. The life span of such bits is variable: some last for days, some for hours, and others disintegrate in a few minutes. Such fragmentation takes place in nature wherever living things are found. Fragments of this sort are akin to subvital structures. These structures often arise in a complex multimolecular environment. The combination of subvital structures in a multimolecular environment constituted the prerequisite condition for the origin of life in the first place; this condition has continued to exist ever since. The environment of the cells of multicellular organisms is rich in organic compounds. Local regions of the outside environment, whether land or water, become temporarily highly enriched in complex organic compounds and systems upon the death and dissolution or the mechanical disruption therein of an organism. Thus, the general prerequisite for the origin of life—the presence of complex macromolecular systems in a suitable environment—has continued to exist ever since life first began.

3. The Irreversibility of Evolution

The proposition that evolution proceeds irreversibly is sound. This concept is well developed in a thoughtful and thought-provoking book by H. Blum.[11] In Blum's book, the second law of thermodynamics is applied to evolution. Concerning every stage in evolution, it may be said that its history has been left behind, never again to be repeated, but that the history has imprinted its stamp on the present. Neobiogenesis is consistent with this view. It does not proclaim that the primeval life recurred again and again through the repeated recurrence of the primeval conditions. Each occurrence of neobiogenesis issues from the materials and conditions of the period and locality as the result of the interplay of forces between a precursor macromolecular system and the environment.

4. Competition Against Pre-existing Organisms

This line of argument claims that no newly arising form can withstand the competition against the already adapted forms in the fierce struggle for existence. The validity of this argument is firmly and universally believed, and has been expressed by many people at various times. Darwin, too, gave voice to it. He stated his reasons for disbelieving spontaneous generation as follows: "It is often said that all the conditions for the first production of a living organism are now present, which could ever have been present. But if (and oh! what a big if!) we could conceive in some warm little pond, with all sorts of ammonia and phosphoric salts, light, heat, electricity, &c., present, that a proteine compound was chemically formed ready to undergo still more complex changes, at the present day such matter would be instantly devoured or absorbed, which would not have been the case before living creatures were formed." We owe to Garrett Hardin[12] the rediscovery of this remarkable observation. It has been much quoted since its rediscovery. The validity of this statement bears closer scrutiny in the light of present knowledge.

Neobiogenesis does not depend on the recreation of all the conditions originally responsible for the formation of the first living organism. Perhaps it should be said again that it is not to be imagined (granting the possibility of neobiogenesis) that each neobiont has to repeat the whole history of the first living thing or to arrive on the scene as an exact replica or even a reasonable facsimile of it. Neobionts arise out of the complex organic milieu of the particular period in which they occur and will have properties stamped upon them that are determined by the physicochemical nature of the system from which they arise. Their activities will also reflect the extent of the biochemical evolution of the period.

One cannot grant neobiogenesis and say simultaneously that no neobiont can survive anywhere on earth at any time under any conditions since life first began. The neobiont must be alive. It must have the characteristics of a living thing. Under at least some earthly conditions the neobiont theoretically must be capable of a metabolism that would permit the neobiont to maintain itself, grow, and reproduce. If this is not granted, neobiogenesis has not been granted. Further, if it is so granted, it must also be accepted that the neobiont comes into being where the minimum requirements for its existence are to be found. Only when that is done can the argument rightfully proceed to the next step, namely, that pre-existing organisms, already adapted to that environment and requiring the same minimum conditions, will *always* win out over the neobiont in the competition for the things that make for survival. Such a neobiont is a tailor-made strawman to be knocked down. But we are talking about nature-made neobionts, not man-made ones with conveniently built-in vulnerability or nonviability. The argument is not valid that an organism just because it is newly arisen will have no adaptive features or survival value anywhere any time under any conditions. Such a view oversimplifies the struggle-for-existence concept and ignores interspecies compatibility and aid. Moreover, it assumes that at all times in every biological niche the organisms to be found therein are so adapted as to survive against any invader. That this view is not valid hardly needs to be argued, as the succession of forms in ecological niches is a well-documented phenomenon.

The original living thing or things, the eobionts, had to have a manner of existence based entirely on an inanimate environment. But ever since then, newly arising forms have had other organisms in increasing variety with which, on which, or in which to live. Neobionts have a wider choice of metabolic patterns in which to exist than did eobionts. Newly arising organisms with metabolic deficiencies can survive *in the presence of other living things* although such new organisms could not survive *in an inanimate world.* Neobionts may be commensalistic, symbiotic, or parasitic, as well as free-living. Once neobiogenesis is granted, there seems no logical way of denying the persistence of at least some of the large number of conceivable neobionts.

5. Biochemical Similarities Among All Living Things

There is a remarkable similarity in the biochemistry and metabolism of all living things. This similarity has been taken to mean that life originated only once in the past with a given chemical composition and metabolic pathways. This structure and metabolism were then handed down to all subsequent living things by reproduction with occasional mutation. If life had originated again and again in the past, the argument goes, we would expect to find today lines of organisms with distinctly different chemical structures and metabolic pathways. We will now examine the validity of this argument against the possibility that neobiogenesis has occurred or is occurring.

Chemical Similarity. The chemicals of which all living things are composed are essentially the same. All have proteins, carbohydrates, nucleic acids, lipids, coenzymes, and certain other substances in common. The first three are polymeric, that is, each is composed of a large number of subunits that are chemically combined. The similarity among the subunits is truly striking. Proteins from any organism are composed of the same 18–20 subunits, the amino acids. Moreover, although amino acids can exist in either of two enantiomorphic states, D- or L- (Chapter 7), the amino acids in all living things are L-amino acids. Likewise, carbohydrates in all living things are composed of D-sugars. As for nucleic acids, the same few nucleotides make up the great variety of nucleic acids found in all organisms. The number of subunits which make up the various lipids are also limited and common to all life.

It is pointed out that the evidence from cofactors and prosthetic groups of enzymes is equally striking. Many enzymes require the simultaneous presence of some other compound or compounds to bring about the appropriate action. These are relatively few in number compared to the great number and variety of enzymes that depend on cofactors. In other words, the same cofactor may serve a number of different and even unrelated enzymes. Cofactors found in the lowest forms of life may also be found in the highest forms (plant or animal).

Metabolic Similarity. The evidence from a comparison of metabolic pathways is thought to be perhaps even more convincing. Considering the obvious morphological and functional differences between animals and plants or between microorganisms and macroorganisms, it might be expected that wide differences would exist in the metabolism of these forms. However, although differences do exist, they are not as marked as the great similarities. Moreover, where metabolic pathways or mechanisms are present, they are identical or similar regardless of species. These metabolic pathways are as follows: breakdown of hexoses to trioses, protein and nucleic acid synthesis, fatty acid oxidation, fatty acid and amino acid synthesis, urea formation, the citric acid cycle, the "pentose shunt," and others.

The sum total of the biochemical evidence seems to point irrefutably to a single origin of life that incorporated a particular biochemical structure and pattern of reactions. All subsequent organisms are said to have inherited this structure and pattern, thus making for the obvious interrelatedness of all organisms in spite of the superficial diversity introduced by mutations.

Refutation. The great strength of the biochemical evidence, however, lies in a premise, not necessarily correct, that was used also in the previous arguments against the possibility of neobiogenesis. This is the assumption that each neobiont must originate in exactly the same fashion as did the original eobiont. It is supposed that each re-origin has to start with the conversion of simple gases into simple organic compounds, then the simple organic compounds into complex ones, and these into prevital systems, which finally give rise to a new living thing. But this is not a valid premise. Ever since life first arose, there have always been macromolecular systems in a multimolecular environment from which life could have started anew.

Granted, life could not originate until complex macromolecules and a multimolecular organic environment were formed. The whole of the previous chemical evolution was required to produce this stage, but it is no longer required. Complex organic compounds of all kinds have existed since life first began. In addition, living things have increased the variety of those that are biochemically significant. Subvital structures of all manner are also to be found. Thus, the possibility of the origin of life from a complex but inanimate beginning has always been present since the first organisms arose.

Moreover, each case of neobiogenesis, arising out of the substances and metabolic pathways characteristic of a period, would establish neobionts with a structure and metabolism characteristic of the organisms of that period. Therefore, the expectation expressed by the opponents of neobiogenesis that neobiogenesis should establish lines of organisms with D-amino acids, L-sugars, and other biochemical characteristics, distinctly different from existing organisms, is entirely mistaken.

6. The Lack of Observed Cases of Neobiogenesis

Actually, this is the only valid argument against neobiogenesis. The wealth of organic compounds and macromolecular systems available today should have resulted in neobiogenesis frequently enough to have been authentically reported by this time. However, there is this difficulty; every living microorganism found is presumed to have come from some pre-existing microorganisms. Neobiogenesis could conceivably take place and the neobiont be written off as the result of contamination.

Consequences of Neobiogenesis

The presence of simple microorganisms furnishes an indirect support for neobiogenesis. It would be more reasonable to assume that such simple forms of life have arisen only recently than that they have descended, relatively unchanged, through two billion or more years. Bacteria, for example, undergo mutation at an appreciable rate; considering their extremely short reproductive cycle, the opportunity for evolution is as great for these microorganisms as for any other organisms.

The supposition is not entirely unwarranted that life at a very primitive level (neobiont) continued to arise ever since the first living things came into being. Neobionts are subject to evolutionary changes, and the earliest of them have long since evolved into higher forms or have become extinct. The bacteria of today are recent arrivals on the scene, some earlier than others, but all destined to evolve further or to become extinct. The population of bacteria of the future (thousands or millions of years hence) will come about through the evolution of neobionts even now forming.

Another possible outcome of neobiogenesis is that the interrelatedness among organisms may be more limited than we now suppose. For example, the Animal and Plant Kingdoms may have no common ancestry. Each may have had its separate beginnings in neobionts unrelated to each other except for the fact that each arose from a complex chemical milieu. Further, some of the phyla in each Kingdom may have no ancestry in common with the other phyla of that Kingdom. The difficulties met in constructing a single taxonomic scheme embracing all organisms past and present may be due to the possibility that the discontinuities in such schemes are real and represent the existence of separate lines of descent from independent neobiogenic events at different times in the history of the earth down to the present.*

The purpose of examining the case against neobiogenesis, however, was to evaluate the validity of the negative evidence, and not to prove neobiogenesis as a fact. No matter how convinced one may be by the arguments that neobiogenesis is not impossible, there is nothing in them to prove that it *does* take place. Neobiogenesis may really be impossible. But if that is so, it is for reasons other than those now advanced.

*Many of the ideas on neobiogensis in this chapter were first expressed in an article in *Science* in 1960.[9] The possibility of organisms arising de novo has also been touched on by Fox.[13]

References

1. Drake, F. D., "Project Ozma," *Sky and Telescope* **19,** 3 (1962).
2. Shapley, H., "Of Stars and Men," Beacon, Boston, 1958.
3. Shapley, H., "View from a Distant Star," Basic Books Inc., New York, 1963.
4. Huang, Su-Shu, *Sci. Am.* **202,** 55 (1960).
5. Moore, P., and Jackson, F., "Life in the Universe," W. W. Norton and Co., New York, 1962.
6. Ovendon, N. W., "Life in the Universe," Anchor Book, Doubleday and Co., Inc., Garden City, N. Y., 1962.
7. Simpson, G. G., *Science* **143,** 769 (1964).
8. Blum, H. F., *Am. Scientist* **49,** 474 (1961).
9. Keosian, J., *Science* **131,** 479 (1960).
10. Pasteur, L., *Compt. rend.* **50,** 303, 674, 849 (1860); ibid **51,** 348 (1860); ibid **56,** 734 (1863); *Ann. Chim. et phys.* **3,** 64 (1862).
11. Blum, H. F., "Time's Arrow and Evolution," 2nd ed. revised, Harpers & Row Publishers, New York, 1962.
12. Hardin, G., *Sci. Monthly* **70,** 178 (1950).
13. Fox, S. W., *Science* **132,** 200 (1960).

Selected Readings

Bernal, J. D., "The Physical Basis of Life," Routledge and Kegan Paul, London, 1949.

Blum, H. F., in Rudnick, D., ed., "Rhythmic and Synthetic Growth Processes," Princeton University Press, Princeton, N. J., 1957.

———, "Time's Arrow and Evolution," 2nd ed. revised, Harper & Row Publishers, New York, 1962.

Ehrensvärd, G., "Life: Origin and Development," The University of Chicago Press, Chicago, 1962.

Haldane, J. B. S., "Science and Human Life," Harper Brothers, New York, 1933.

"Modern Ideas on Spontaneous Generation," Annals of the N. Y. Acad. of Sciences, Vol. 69, 1957.

Moore, P., and Jackson, F., "Life in the Universe," W. W. Norton & Company, Inc., New York, 1962.

Oparin, A. I., "Proiskhozhdenie zhizni," Moscow, 1924.

In Russian, not translated. This is the first publication in book form of Oparin's ideas on the origin of life. The major points of his theory are briefly explained in it.

———, "The Origin of Life on Earth," MacMillan, New York, 1938.

This book is a translation by Sergius Morgulis of the book by Oparin published in 1936 in Moscow. The salient features of Oparin's theory are more fully discussed in this book.

———, "The Origin of Life," Dover Publications, Inc., New York, 1953 ($1.75).

This book is an exact reprint of the 1938 edition except for a new introduction by Sergius Morgulis.

———, "The Origin of Life on the Earth," Academic Press, New York, 1957.

A restatement by Oparin of his theory of the origin of life in terms of the work and discussion on the subject since the publication of the 1936 edition. It is a translation by Ann Synge of the Russian edition also published in 1957.

———, "Life: Its Nature, Origin and Development," Academic Press, New York, 1962.

    This book is a much condensed version of the 1957 edition but includes an evaluation of some further experimental work which bears on the theory of the origin of life.

———, "The Chemical Origin of Life," Charles C. Thomas, Springfield, Ill. (1964.) Translated from the Russian by Ann Synge.

Ovenden, M. W., "Life in the Universe," Anchor Book by Doubleday & Co., Inc., Garden City, N. Y., 1962.

Rutten, M. G., "The Geological Aspects of the Origin of Life on Earth," Elsevier Publishing Co., Amsterdam, New York, 1962.

Schäfer, E. A., Presidential Address to the Brit. Assoc. Adv. Science, 1912.

Shapley, H., "The View From a Distant Star," Basic Books, Inc., Publishers, New York, 1963.

"Stars and Galaxies," Page, T., ed., A Spectrum Book, Prentice-Hall, Inc., Englewood Cliffs, N. J., 1962.

Urey, H. C., "The Planets," Yale University Press, New Haven, Conn., 1952.

Wald, G., "The Origin of Life," *Sci. Am.* (August, 1954).

Index